County Ambulance

Fifty Years of Service

1948 - 1999

A Nostalgia Road Special

by

Mike Leonard

NOSTALGIA ROAD

Durham County Ambulance
Fifty Years Of Service

The **Nostalgia Road** Series ™
is conceived, designed and published
by

Trans-Pennine Publishing Ltd.

PO Box 10
Appleby-in-Westmorland
Cumbria,   CA16 6FA
Tel. 017683 51053 Fax. 017683 53558
e-mail trans.pennine@virgin.net
(A Quality Guild registered company)

Reprographics
Barnabus Design & Repro
Threemilestone, Truro
Cornwall, TR4 9AN
01872 241185

And Printed in Cumbria by
Kent Valley Colour Printers Ltd.
Shap Road Industrial Estate
Kendal, Cumbria LA9 6NZ
01539 741344

Front Cover:
*A 1965 Commer Civil Defence Ambulance (a type of chassis
once used by Durham County Ambulance Service) with one
of the new Ford Lunar ambulances on the north-east coast.*
A. Crosskill
Rear Cover Top:
*The Chester-le-Street District Ambulance of 1919, operated
by the Red Cross/St. John joint committee*   **E Walton**
Rear Cover Bottom:
One of the Renault Traffic outpatient ambulances.
Title Page:
Lanchester Depot based at Maiden Law Hospital c1938

House Of Commons
London SW1A 0AA

Dear reader,

I am very pleased to write this introduction in support of the Durham County Ambulance Service as it celebrates 50 years of service to the people of County Durham. The men and women of the Ambulance Service do a wonderful job which often goes unnoticed, but their care and skills are very much appreciated.

This book sets out in an interesting and informative way, the great progress made over 50 years by Durham County Ambulance Service. It highlights the growth and development of the Service within the National Health Service since its inception 50 years ago.

I send the Service my very best wishes for the future.

Tony Blair

The Rt. Hon. Tony Blair, MP,
Prime Minister

Left:
A Bedford K1 Ambulance outside Durham's Dryburn Hospital c1950.

Right:
The author, ADO Mike Leonard demonstrates the service's equipment to the Prime Minister Tony Blair who is, of course, the Member of Parliament for Sedgefield, Co. Durham.

1

Introduction

The Durham County Ambulance Service was born out of proposals for the National Health Service under Section 27 of the National Health Service Act 1946, which came into effect on 5th July 1948. However, this service did not simply materialise overnight; nor did it spring up, as if by magic, for it had a long and honourable genesis. Yet in this genesis there was great diversity, as prior to 1948 local ambulance services were provided by a large number of differing bodies. In addition to local authorities and hospitals, services were operated by benevolent mine owners, miner's lodges, local philanthropic groups, and the various first-aid organisations to name but a few. All of these provided some sort of service, generally with the aim of communal good, but there was little if any form of co-operation or standard of service. As the 20th century dawned, considerable progress had been made towards the provision of ambulance services in County Durham, but to understand the history we must go back even further to the very concept of this type of service.

In 1870 Henri Dunant, a Swiss Banker and founder of the International Red Cross developed the concept of an ambulance service, a service that would be responsible for the care and transport of sick and injured people. One of the first regions in Great Britain to adopt this idea was London, which formed the London Police Horse Ambulance Service in 1899. No special facilities were provided for the stabling of these vehicles, and they were accommodated at hospitals by day and fire stations at night.

Within four years ambulance services had been established in cities such as Leeds, Bradford, Sheffield, Liverpool and Birmingham and many other areas were making progress towards establishing their own civic or municipal services. In 1909 the Municipal Ambulance Services Act gave powers to certain Health Authorities (which, in those days, were under local authority control), to establish ambulance services. In 1915 the London County Council Ambulance Service was formed, and it is believed to be the first established under the authority of a County Council. Legal powers to establish ambulance services were extended to all local Health Authorities by 1922, a situation that existed until 1948.

The ambulance services established under the 1922 Act varied by individual local authority, as did the inclination with regard to the method of financing them, but by and large they were on a repayment basis whereby the patient was charged for the use of the ambulance.

The National Health Services Act 1946, which came into effect on 5th July 1948, included as Section 27 an obligation on County Councils and County Borough Councils, to provide an ambulance service within their authority areas. The significant difference being that the provision of these services would be funded through taxation and local rates, rather than being charged directly to those patients actually using the ambulance. For the first time, free ambulance services were to be provided to all sectors of the community as part of the new welfare state.

Theoretically every community, no matter how remote, now had access to a public ambulance for both emergency and (under certain guidelines) outpatient travel to and from hospital. Even then the understanding of what was required from an ambulance service was far different from what we know today. Not unnaturally there was considerable abuse of the 'free transport', by both patients and medical staff alike and it took ambulance professionals some considerable time to get the 'end-users' to understand what duties the new service was obligated to fulfil.

Whilst ever there was a view that the ambulance service was little more than a medical taxi service, it is not surprising that the decision-makers did not see fit to provide the type of resources that were actually required by those at the forefront of pre-hospital care. In those early days ambulancemen were looked upon merely as drivers and all too often the ambulances were viewed like any other municipal vehicle. Some authorities painted them in the same liveries as the council lorries, others gave crews the same uniforms as bus drivers, and elsewhere some even kept their ambulances in the same garage as the corporation dustcarts.

In his book, **NHS Ambulances - The First 25 Years** (also published by Trans-Pennine), the noted ambulance historian Chris Batten comments; 'Ambulance crews were normally thought of merely as drivers with the only qualification being an ability to drive. Generally, only a basic knowledge of first aid training was given to the crews. This concept lasted for a long time and made it difficult for ambulancemen to achieve recognition for their profession.'

Glorified deliverymen perhaps, who at best offered little more than a scoop and run service in times of serious emergency! In saying this, we are not casting any aspersions on the dedication of the men (after World War II there were very few women) operating the service, but merely reflecting on the inadequacy of the training and equipment with which they were provided. Through the dark years of World War II, especially in the blitzed cities, this concept of scoop and run had been perpetuated, for expediency dictated that the casualties be removed from the danger areas as quickly as possible. The risks that this could pose to a casualty were all too often overlooked and the significance of the 'Golden Hour', in which a patient should be assessed and treated after trauma, was not appreciated. Even if those offering pre-hospital care appreciated it, the significance of good 'first aid training' was lost in the higher chains of command at both Westminster and in the corridors of the local Town or County halls.

The problems of fusing the differing types of ambulance provision into a cohesive service as part of a National Health Service can not be underestimated, due to the chronic shortage of vehicles in 1948 which combined with the poor quality in training for the staff. Each county authority was allowed to organise the new service in its own way, within overall guidelines, but a clause in the NHS Act allowed local authorities to enlist the voluntary services of bodies like the British Red Cross and the St. John Ambulance Brigade. In many rural areas, and in some large towns, the use of these 'agency' services allowed the county councils valuable time to organise their services. Indeed, so professional were these agency services, that they were allowed to continue for a number of years.

Yet, it must be said that move towards change was slow, and it would take some significant time even to accelerate the process. Then, one day in 1952 a simple, but moving, photograph appeared in almost every major newspaper in the western world, and sowed the seeds for a change in thinking. Having been circulated by the Associated Press, this image accompanied the news report of England's worst-ever rail disaster, which occurred when three trains piled into one another at Harrow & Wealdstone Station in the early morning rush hour on 8th October. In all 112 people died, and hundreds of survivors were sent to hospital by whatever means could be found. Those who walked out of the wreckage with minor injuries were needlessly put into the first ambulances and sent to nearby hospitals. However, as the more serious were extricated from the debris (and with all the ambulances gone), badly injured people were carried on carriage seat cushions and placed in commandeered vehicles. Even a passing removal van was 'flagged down' by the police and pressed into service, while other casualties were sent to hospitals where no accident facilities existed. It is safe to say that the magnitude of this one event completely overwhelmed the emergency services, and in so doing it exposed a glaring hole in major disaster response.

Top Left:
The Darlington Fire Brigade's horse ambulance pictured leaving the station at the turn of the century. This building would, in later years, serve as the town's ambulance station after the firemen moved to new premises.
Courtesy: Ron Henderson
Below:
Pedal Power; a cycle ambulance litter c1900 believed to be of military origins.

On that same Autumn morning a young Afro-American nurse serving at a nearby United States Army Air force base, was seen tending a severely injured man on the platform. It was just one of the many victims that Abbie Sweetwine assisted that day, but it was the photo of nurse and victim that appeared in newspapers around the globe. In the incident Nurse Sweetwine and her colleagues were applying the technique of triage, which was little known in Britain at the time. However, the American's work of assessing the severity of the injuries sustained by the casualties, and the prioritising of ambulance transport according to their needs, undoubtedly saved many lives that day.

The public inquiry that followed showed that the aftercare at Harrow & Wealdstone was found wanting, but it also commended the American military's triage system and suggested that it should be examined and evaluated for possible implementation in other disaster situations. The press coverage of the NHS response was very critical, and for the first time senior ambulance personnel had a lever (public opinion) that they could effectively employ in the development of a professional and well-equipped service. It was to take a long time in coming, and there were many obstacles to overcome along the way, but change was destined to occur. There will be few ambulance professionals today who will recall the significance that the Harrow Disaster played in reaching the level of service we now enjoy, but we can safely conclude that out of this one day of adversity came the much needed impetus for change.

In the pages that follow, this book traces the evolution and development of the ambulance service in County Durham, starting with its position prior to 1948 running though to the present day. To tell the story we split the 50 years of history into two distinct parts, each of 25 years in duration. We will also look at the developments we can expect for the future of this and other ambulance services throughout the country.

The next important change in ambulance provision within County Durham came in 1974 when ambulance services transferred fully into the National Health Service, coming out of local authority control and into the care of District Health Authorities. This coincided with boundary changes for local authorities, so the new service after 1974 operated in a smaller geographical area and with a much-reduced population from that served prior to this time. For example the population recorded for Co. Durham in 1956 was 1,500,000 whereas in 1998 the number is (at 593,000) little more than a third of that figure. Yet despite the changing face of the county, its ambulance service was to face new pressures and challenges.

The second half of our history looks at the changes reorganisation in 1974 brought about, and it concludes with the new pressures and challenges that face the service as it undergoes one further change at the end of its fifty year history. Above all this is a history that is dedicated to the many men and women, from all sectors of the community that have delivered ambulance and pre-hospital care to people of County Durham during the last half century. On the dawn of a new millennium and at the end of an era, it is perhaps just as important to look back into our heritage as we continue to look forward to the future development of our service to the public.

Above:
Contrasts in motor ambulances can be seen with the comparison of these two pictures taken 90 years apart. Few details are known about this Renault ambulance with solid wheels and open cab c1905, but 80 years later Durham would acquire more modern Renault Ambulances.

Left:
A 1996 Ford Transit Diesel with a UVG Lazer body, standing next to a Honda ST1100 Pan European Rapid Response paramedic motorcycle at Durham's Dryburn Hospital.

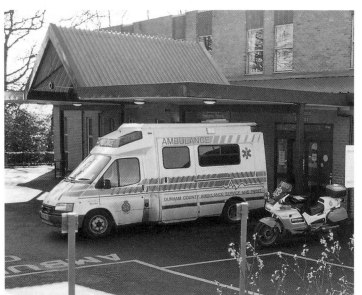

THE FIRST 25 YEARS
The Formation Of The County Council Service.

Once formed under the auspices of Durham County Council in 1948 a degree of unification and standardisation began, but due to post-war vehicle shortages, staff shortages and rationing, it was a long time before a modern ambulance service could be developed for Durham's residents. Within County Durham these facilities were, to say the least, virtually basic prior to 1948; and it was such poor facilities that the Council took over that July. Unfortunately, a lack of building materials prevented the provision of dedicated ambulance stations, and for a long while staff facilities remained inadequate on a number of counts.

It can be safely said that many authorities fared worse than Durham, and that the fleets they inherited were little more than relics and/or badly overworked after six years of war, during which period the lack of maintenance and spares had been commonplace. The types of vehicles employed differed greatly, as prior to 1948 ambulance services had been provided by a number of disparate bodies. In County Durham these included the County District Councils and Joint Hospital Boards, the Ministry of Health, the County Council, miners lodges and welfare schemes, voluntary bodies, private mine owners (later the National Coal Board), other industrial firms and private hirers. The table opposite shows the number of ambulances in use in Durham immediately prior to the introduction of the County service in 1948 and their respective ages.
Below:
There was little money available for ambulance provision during the depressed years of the 1920s and early '30s and this Chester-le-Street ambulance of 1933 shows evidence of this with a 'bald' spare tyre.
Courtesy Enid Walton

Table 1:
Analysis of ambulance owners, vehicle ages and staff employed

Owners	Age In Years					Total	Staff	
	0-4	5-8	9-12	13-16	16+		F/T -	P/T
County District Councils & Joint Hospital Boards (General Cases	9	4	7	3	5	28	29	28
CDC and JHB - (Infectious Cases)	1	2	12	4	3	22	20	27
Ministry of Health Dryburn Emergency Hospital		2	2	-	-	4	4	-
Ministry of Health - Winterton Emergency Hospital	-	1	-	-	-	1	2	3
County Council Tuberculosis	-	-	1	-	-	1	2	1
Miners Lodges and Welfare Schemes	1	6	9	4	8	28	18	35
Voluntary bodies other than above	5	6	9	2	1	23	15	32
National Coal Board	1	1	20	5	19	46	48	120
Industrial firms (other than NCB)	-	1	-	3	-	1	5	10	5
Private Hirers	1	-	1	2	1	5	15	19
TOTALS	**19**	**23**	**63**	**20**	**39**	**164**	**162**	**270**

Many of these ambulances were used to provide services on a repayment basis and others on a subscription basis, but funding for these services was always restricted. Slightly better ambulances were provided by many of the privately owned coal mining companies prior to nationalisation under the National Coal Board, and some maintained both a colliery ambulance and a doctor for use by their employees (and families).

A typical subscription cost for the 'miners' health club' (the name varied from pit to pit) would be 6d (2.5p) per week, which would be deducted from the miner's wage packet to cover a family of four.

As a consequence of the widely differing level of coverage and availability, the provision of ambulance services on a consistent and universal basis became part of the overall proposals for the formation of the National Health Service. In the lead up to the formation of a County Ambulance Service, Durham County Council produced a development plan. The main features of this very comprehensive document are as follows:

i   It was decided that the number of vehicles in use prior to implementation was (at 164) too many. Of this number, many were not being used to their full capacity and it was considered that with a co-ordinated service the number required would be about two-thirds of the inherited ambulance fleet.

ii It was proposed that the service should be under the administrative control of the County Medical Officer (CMO) and that an Ambulance Officer (responsible to the CMO) should be appointed together with clerical officers to supervise the arrangements.

iii The majority of the vehicles on the service (61) would be under the direct control of the Local Health Authority and 27 ambulances (owned by 20 voluntary bodies) would be included in the County Service on an agency basis.

iv The remaining ambulances used within the County would not come within the Local Health Authority's service at that time.

v   For operational purposes it was proposed to group ambulances into 17 operational units (see table 2).

vi Each ambulance unit would have a control, which would receive calls and transmit instructions to drivers. Of the control centres to be established, some would be open 24-hours, the remainder being open during the day and their functions at other times being taken over by the 24-hour control centres.

vii It was considered that there were too many ambulance stations to allow a desirable concentration of vehicles, but that this could not be remedied without new buildings and adaptation, which could not be undertaken immediately.

viii The staff employed by voluntary bodies in the discharge of agency duties would be mutually agreed when the agency arrangements were made.

ix Staff employed by the County Council would include an Ambulance Officer, administrative assistants and the necessary drivers and control staff.

x   The authority would make arrangements to ensure that, as far as possible, ambulance drivers and attendants would hold a first aid certificate. This certification would be from the St. John Ambulance Association or the British Red Cross Society or other such first aid qualification as might be approved or prescribed by the Minister of Health. (However, a driving test was the only selection criterion that was used in the recruitment procedure at that time).

xi In addition all drivers and attendants should be trained so as to be interchangeable in their duties.

In the formation of its plan the Council made the following wordy statement:

'In order to provide adequately for the conveyance, where necessary, at any time of the day or night of persons suffering from illness, or mental defectiveness or expectant or nursing mothers from places in the County to places in or outside the County and to meet the Council's obligations to neighbouring Local Health Authorities under arrangements for joint user or for mutual assistance in emergency, the service both provided directly and through the agency of voluntary organisations, will comprise 75 to 95 ambulances, 6 to 20 sitting case cars, and 108 to 286 whole-time drivers and attendants supplemented by part-time services of volunteers. The Council intends to develop the service up to the minima mentioned as rapidly as circumstances permit.

The requirements of the ambulance service will be kept under constant review, and such adjustments as experience shows are required will be made from time to time within the limits indicated above in the number of ambulances, sitting case cars and staff. Such temporary redistribution of vehicles and staff between the stations will be made as may from time to time be deemed necessary to ensure the most effective use of the authority's ambulance resources.'

To oversee the service, Mr Richard Birch was appointed as the Ambulance Officer for Durham, and he went on to become Chief Ambulance Officer, a post that he retained until his retirement on 13th October 1963.

Below:
The body of the Darlington horse ambulance, pictured on page 2, is seen below having been remounted on a Ford chassis. This situation of recyling bodies from horse vehicles was fairly typical of the era as it represented a considerable saving on purchasing new bodies.
Courtesy: Ron Henderson

Above:
This Napier was the first motor ambulance used by the St. John Ambulance Association, and named after Harvey Reeves, the Mayor of Northampton, who promoted its purchase.

Once operational, the cases dealt with were found to fall into two main categories, namely: -
(a) accident and urgent maternity cases, etc., and
(b) patients for admission to, or discharge from, hospital; non-urgent maternity cases; persons suffering from infectious diseases; cases attending hospital out-patient departments; and occasionally a patient requiring transport to a distant location.

In the latter group the conditions governing the provision for transport were that the ambulance or car was requisitioned personally from a hospital or by a doctor, nurse, midwife or dentist, or by the patient (on the production of a medical certificate supporting the need for transport).

However, at the beginning of the scheme it soon became evident that the public needed to be clearly informed of the correct procedure for summoning an ambulance. So, to meet this need some 4,000 notices were printed and distributed to hospitals, doctors, dentists, nurses, midwives, health visitors, child welfare centres, libraries, police stations, and factories etc. where they were to be displayed in prominent positions.

That the Durham service was well used is supported by statistics for its first year. By the end of 1948, having operated for just six months, the service had covered 552,486 miles and carried 40,298 patients with the use of the following facilities and staff:

Driver attendants	118	Ambulance depots	42
Clerk telephonists	27	Ambulance controls	9
Headquarters staff	7	Ambulances	72
		Sitting-case cars	2
Total Staff Employed	152		

Table 2;
Unit Areas & Resources
Authorised and Achieved by 31st December 1948

UNIT AREA	AUTHORISED			ACTUAL		
	Amb's	Cars	Drivers	Amb's	Cars	Drivers
1 East Tyneside	8	2	26	7	-	8
2 West Tyneside	5	1	16	5	-	6
3 Stanley #	7	2	18	6	-	8
4 Consett	6	2	14	4	-	6
5 North Eastern #	4	1	14	4	-	6
6 Houghton	4	1	12	3	-	8
7 Seaham #	4	1	12	3	-	6
8 Easington	12	1	20	7	-	10
9 Hartlepool #	1	-	8	1	-	1
10 Sedgefield #	5	1	14	4	-	5
11 Stockton	7	1	25	6	-	17
12 Darlington *	-	-	-	-	-	-
13 Barn'd Castle #	2	1	10	2	-	2
14 B'p Auckland	8	2	16	5	-	10
15 Chester-le-St #	4	1	12	3	-	5
16 Durham	13	2	34	10	2	16
17 Western #	5	1	12	2	-	-
TOTALS	**95**	**20**	**263**	**72**	**2**	**118**

Notes:
\# Day controls until 15th December 1948
* County Service reinforced by adjoining
Darlington County Borough Service as required.

Above:
*Joe Broadbent with Spennymoor Urban Council's Austin ambulance,
(Fleet No.25), just prior to the 1948 formation.*

The following extract from the Chief Medical Officer's Report at the end of the year gives a considerable insight into how the service was organised and operated in that first six months: -
'A comparison of the figures shows that the present service is meeting a demand greater than that previously met by more than twice the number of vehicles, and it is reasonable to assume that, as the general public becomes aware of the facilities now made available, a substantial increase on these figures for ambulance and car transport will occur in the future.'

The report then broke down the overall position into a number of key areas, and for the sake of presenting a detailed picture of the infant service, we include several important parts of the report verbatim.
'ORGANISATION :
(a) Controls.
The control duties were at first shared between eight 'day' controls (operating between 9am and 5pm and manned by staff of the county district councils) and nine '24-hour' controls, but as from 15th December 1948 it was found possible to close the day controls and operate the service from the '24-hour' controls only. For operational purposes the drivers and vehicles are grouped into 17 unit areas and these areas are, in turn, further grouped into the nine control areas. Seven of the controls are under the direct control of the County Council, while two - Darlington and West Hartlepool - act as agents in the scheme. Each control is continually manned throughout the 24-hours, and its function is to receive calls for ambulance transport and transmit the necessary instructions to the head driver in charge of the drivers and vehicles available for duty in the appropriate unit area. Each unit area has an emergency-duty ambulance on a 24-hour availability while the balance of the vehicles operate in the 'general' service.

(b) Depots.
There are at present 42 ambulance depots functioning in the county and active steps are being taken to reduce this number to a working minimum by concentrating the men and vehicles at the most convenient working point in each unit area - many of the so-called depots are actually no more than garages for the vehicles. Until the building position becomes easier, however, there is little prospect of obtaining new depots, and consequently, while the best of the existing depots will continue in use, every effort is being made to find more suitable temporary accommodation in other cases.
(c) Vehicles:
Most of the vehicles in the service are directly operated by the County Council, and have been assisted by nine vehicles, which were operated for the Council by seven 'agencies'. One agency (Roddymoor, Crook) withdrew its vehicle from the scheme on 23rd October, while a second (Ferryhill) terminated its services on 1st November, but sold its vehicle to the Council and the driver was appointed on the county staff. On 5th July the scheme started with a total of 76 ambulances and one car, and this number has been gradually reinforced by purchases during the subsequent months; the total being made up as follows: -

	Ambulances	Cars	Total
Transferred from County District Councils And Joint Hospital Boards	48	-	48
Owned by 10 welfare organisations and operated for the Council on the basis of the reimbursement of actual expenditure, pending purchase.	15	-	15
Owned by seven 'agencies' and operating for the Council on payment of a mileage rate.	9		9
Purchased by the Council	10	1	11
Owned previously by the Council	2	-	2
Gifts to the Council	2	-	2
Totals	**86**	**1**	**87**

The average age of the vehicles is approximately ten years, and great difficulty has been experienced in keeping them in active service. Of the total of 86 ambulances, 14 were unserviceable by the end of the year and one agency withdrew its vehicle during the period under review. There were thus available for duty on the 31st December only 72 ambulances and two cars, a further second-hand car having been purchased in December. From the 5th July, minor repairs had to be undertaken on 73 of the vehicles while 32 required major repairs. To ease the vehicle situation, a replacement programme dealing with a total of 95 ambulances and 20 cars over a period of the next six years has been adopted, and it is hoped that, following negotiations with the makers, the delivery of new ambulances will start in 1949.

(d) Staff.

The ambulance officer and headquarters staff have had to work in very overcrowded conditions in a single room since the appointed day, but the building of more adequate hutted accommodation has recently been approved. In the meantime staff are to be moved to temporary but more commodious accommodation. The control staff (comprising) 4 clerk-telephonists working a three-shift system man each of the seven county controls over the 24-hours. Every effort is being made to improve the accommodation in which they work and to provide simple amenities. On the 5th July the total of driver-attendants available for duty was 76, of which 10 were employed in a part-time capacity. The number appointed between the 5th July and the end of the year was 58 (including 4 holiday relief drivers) making a total of 134 driver attendants. The employment of the part-time and holiday relief drivers terminated in the course of the period and, including three resignations from the service, the net total employed at the close of the year was 118. The aim is now to provide a crew of two men for each ambulance, as recommended by the Minister of Health, and to this end the establishment has been fixed at a total of 263.'

The CMO's report concluded with the following paragraph:
'I should like to place on record my appreciation of the support given to the scheme by the district councils and their staff since its inauguration, and of the work done by the several voluntary organisations who have placed their ambulances and drivers at the disposal of the County Council as a temporary expedient in the return for the reimbursement of actual reasonable expense incurred. Those voluntary organisations who elected to serve in the scheme on an agency basis have done much good work, and a tribute is due to the drivers of the ambulances, many of whom in the early months of the scheme worked abnormally long hours in order to keep the service going.'

It is clear from this first report that (not unexpectedly), the service provided during the first year had not been without its difficulties. To emphasise this, Joe Broadbent (one of the drivers who transferred on 5th July) recalls that, on the first full day of operation the Bishop Auckland area ambulance did no work whatsoever. The ambulance was based at the Isolation Hospital, South View, Spennymoor, and the new control centre established in Bondgate (controller Wallace Robson), 'forgot they were there'. This type of problem was soon to be remedied when the control centres were combined with ambulance depots at various locations to form 'ambulance stations'. The concept behind these new stations was to provide a co-ordinated, localised service for GPs and hospitals.

Furthermore, with the control centres based in ambulance stations a much tighter control of ambulance usage resulted. They certainly eased the situation and Bishop Auckland finally got its new Ambulance Station at Acacia Road in December 1948, after an interim move to the fire station behind Spennymoor Town Hall, Easington got its new station in 1949. But moves such as this were only small steps in the organisation of an efficient and well-organised service, and much more work was required, as we will discuss under the next four chapter headings.

Organisation, Management and Demand 1948-1973

At the end of 1949 the Chief Medical Officer reported that the service was fully operational and was already showing the increase in demand on transport that had been predicted in the first annual report. At the end of 1949 some 118,353 patients had been carried over a distance of 1.5 million miles. The majority of these cases were described as 'treatment' cases or outpatients as they would be termed today and only 3,749 (just over 3.1%) of the number carried were emergency cases.

The rise in the number of outpatient cases was causing concern nationally and the Minister of Health had been prompted to write to Hospital Management Committees and Boards of Governors to review arrangements and see whether a reduction in the number of calls could be made. The Minister also suggested other measures which could be adopted, but the overall reduction achieved proved not to be material. To cope with the demands in Durham, additions had been made to the staff with the appointment of a Staff Officer to oversee the fieldwork of the personnel. Control arrangements continued with no change and on the overleaf are listed the nine control centres with their respective areas of responsibility.

Above:
Joe Broadbent, who was in at the start (but did no work on the first day), had become a Station Officer when this picture was taken outside the new Bishop Auckland Station in May 1975.

TABLE 3: CONTROL CENTRES, AMBULANCE STATIONS AND AREAS SERVED

Address	Areas Served	Telephone Numbers
Ambulance Control 81, New Elvet DURHAM	Sedgefield Rural District Chester le Street Urban District Chester le Street R.D, Durham Metropolitan Borough. Brandon U.D. Durham R.D (excluding the Civil parish of Rainton), Lanchester R.D. (excluding the Civil parishes of Muggleswick and Healeyfield)	DURHAM 587
Ambulance Station 1, St Johns Road HEBBURN	East Tyneside Jarrow M.B. Hebburn U.D Felling U.D. North Eastern: Washington U.D Boldon U.D Sunderland R.D (that part lying north of the River wear)	HEBBURN 32157
Ambulance Station Villa Real CONSETT	West Tyneside: Whickham U.D. Blaydon U.D. Ryton U.D. Stanley: Stanley U.D Consett U.D. Lanchester R.D. (the Civil parishes of Muggleswick and Healeyfield) Weardale R.D. (the Civil parishes of Hunstanworth and Edmondbyers). Also the township of Blanchland and the parts of Shotley Bridge in Northumberland	CONSETT 411
Ambulance Station Devon Street NEW HERRINGTON	Hetton U.D. Houghton le Spring U.D. Sunderland R.D. (that part lying south of the River Wear) Durham R.D. (the Civil parish of Rainton)	EAST HERRINGTON 3137
Ambulance station Byron Street WHEATLEY HILL	Seaham U.D. Easington R.D.(the Civil parishes of Burdon, Cold Hesledon, Dalton le Dale, East Murton, Seaton-with-Slingley and Warden Law Easington R.D. (the Civil parishes of Castle Eden, Easington, Haswell, Hawthorn, Hutton Henry, Monk Hesledon, Nesbitt, Sheraton-with Hulam, Shotton, Thornley and Wingate).	THORNLEY 243
Ambulance Station York Road HARTLEPOOL	Hartlepool: Hartlepool M.B. Stockton R.D. (the Civil parishes of Brierton, Claxton, Dalton Piercy, Elwick, Elwick Hall, Greatham, Hart, Newton Bewley and Seaton).	HARTLEPOOL 2011
Ambulance Station Barrington House Buchanan Street STOCKTON-ON-TEES	Stockton M.B. Billingham U.D. Stockton R.D. (the Civil parishes of Aislaby, Carlton, Egglescliffe, Elton, Grindon, Longnewton, Newsham, Norton, Preston-on-Tees, Redmarshall and Whitton).	STOCKTON 67410
Ambulance Station DARLINGTON	Darlington: Darlington R.D.	DARLINGTON 3333
Ambulance Station Acacia Road BISHOP AUCKLAND	Barnard Castle:Barnard Castle U.D. Barnard Castle R.D. (excluding the Civil parishes of Bolam, Etherley, Evenwood-and-Barony, Hamsterley and South Bedburn) Bishop Auckland: Bishop Auckland U.D. Shildon U.D. Spennymoor U.D. Barnard Castle R.D. (the Civil parishes of Bolam, Etherley, Evenwood-and-Barony, Hamsterley and South Bedburn).Western: Crook and Willington U.D. Tow Law U.D. Weardale R.D. (excluding the Civil parishes of Hunstanworth and Edmondbyers)	BISHOP AUCKLAND 810

Throughout 1950 the number of patients being carried continued to rise, principally in the transport of outpatients. The total was 159,291 patients, an increase of 40,938 (34%) and the service covered 1,979,682 miles transporting them. In addition the service was called upon to deal with its first major emergency following a serious accident at the Consett Iron Works. This was believed to be an escape of noxious gas, which made the rescue of survivors very hazardous for the emergency services. More than 10 employees of the Iron Works are thought to have been killed immediately and many more seriously injured resulting in an eventual death toll of more than 20 including some of the rescuers. There is no evidence to suggest that ambulance staff were among the casualties of this industrial incident.

The agency arrangement with Middleton-in-Teesdale Home Service Ambulance Scheme was terminated on 30th June 1950, leaving only two agency services at Jarrow and Wheatley Hill. In addition the County Council entered into negotiations with the National Coal Board (NCB) with a view to taking over responsibility for emergency calls arising in the county's mines, thereby removing the anomaly of the NCB operating its own ambulance service within the county area. Agreement in principle was reached and negotiations were then begun to put the proposal into practical effect. This proved to be a very slow process as final agreement was not to be reached on this until 1962.

During 1952 a further huge rise in demand was seen with 293,448 cases carried over 2,268,166 miles, increases of 83,436 (39.7%) and 138,581 (7%) respectively. As in previous years the increase was largely due to yet more outpatient work and the CMO made the following statement:

'It is felt that the demand is not a true indication of the need of ambulance transport in that many patients are conveyed by ambulance who, it would appear, could well make use of the public transport services. In this respect, however, the service has no absolute control over demand, this resting largely with the hospitals and medical practitioners. It was anticipated that the Ministry of Health Circular 30/51 would bring about an appreciable economy in the demand on the service, but the evidence is to the contrary inasmuch as neither hospitals nor doctors appear to be exercising the discrimination advocated in that circular. Early in the year the position was so acute that the County Council was compelled to restrict the carrying of relatives or friends of out-patients except where the patient was a very young child or a blind or deaf person: or where it was considered specially necessary on medical grounds.'

This situation continues to the present day, with much demand placed by people who could well travel by other means, but the service has little if any control on the sanctioning of transport. However, the restrictions on escorts travelling in ambulances remain much the same today.

Because the continuing rise in demand was placing pressure on the staff, vehicles and management, consideration was given (early in 1953) to a review of the existing scheme and the possible need for re-organisation. A special committee was appointed which expressed the view that the general position might be improved and by the year-end detailed proposals were being examined.

Stimulus was given to the committee's recommendations by a visit in March of a fact-finding team from the Ministry of Health. The dramatic rise in patient numbers finally appeared to be abating although a small rise in both numbers and miles travelled was experienced during 1953, and 294,790 patients were carried (+1,342) over 2,286,856 miles (+18,690).

The review of the organisation of the ambulance service, which had been in progress for some time was completed early in 1954. As a result the County Council approved proposed modifications to the organisation that would affect seven main areas of the ambulance service.

Below:
At the end of World War II, there were few new vehicles available for purchase, so a large number of ex-Army lorries were obtained and rebuilt as ambulances at the Home Ambulance Workshops. Most of these had either Austin or Bedford chassis, and can be identified by the heavy duty tyres seen in this picture of Chester-le-Street's 'new' Austin ambulance. It will be noted that this is the same driver as seen in the 1933 picture on page 5, but the tread on his tyres is certainly better.
Courtesy: Enid Walton

DURHAM COUNTY AMBULANCE SERVICE

218

Above: *With the coming of the 1950s, the vehicle supply situation had improved sufficiently for Durham to take delivery of new Bedford K1 chassis with Lomas bodies. Number 218, in its dark green livery, is a classic example of front-line ambulance provision in the county for many years.*   Courtesy Ron Henderson

These changes mentioned on the previous page came in effect from May 1954 onwards, and may be described as follows:

Control system:
Under existing arrangements there were seven controls situated at Bishop Auckland, Consett, Durham, Hebburn, New Herrington, Stockton and Wheatley Hill (in addition to the two agency controls at Darlington and West Hartlepool, which would not be affected by the new proposals). It was proposed that a central control be established at the County HQ in Durham. The central control would have supervisory staff working in shifts to cover the 24-hour period. The depots located at Bishop Auckland, Hebburn, Stanley, Stockton and Wheatley Hill would become message receiving centres, with a telephone operator for each centre during the day shift between Monday and Friday whilst drivers would 'man' the telephone at all other times. Each message-receiving centre would be connected to the central control by a direct telephone line.

Depots:
The three outstations, the New Herrington and Hartlepool depots, the Durham depot and the depots classed as message-receiving centres would provide a 24-hour service. The remaining seven depots would work day shifts only, the shifts being spread over a 12 hour period to meet local conditions. Vehicles from message receiving centres would cover any calls that these depots could not meet during the day, along with those calls occurring when they were closed. It was proposed to close the Lanchester depot and move its vehicles to Durham where they would be used to supplement existing resources or specialist work.

Maintenance:
It was identified that the demands on the service had precluded the establishment of a reserve of vehicles without which a satisfactory maintenance programme could not be conducted. With the additional five vehicles approved, and by improved working arrangements through the reorganisation, it was expected that a satisfactory reserve of vehicles could be established.

Agencies:
Two local authorities (West Hartlepool and Darlington) and one agency then supplemented the County Service. It was proposed that the Wheatley Hill agency with the Hospital Fund ambulance be discontinued, and that

an out-station to assist in the increasing number of calls in the Darlington rural district be established to relieve the continuing and increasing pressure on the Darlington County Borough ambulance. The arrangements with Hartlepool would remain unchanged.

Petrol supplies:

Following a review of fuel supplies additional petrol pump installations were already underway, which would result in petrol supplies for ambulance vehicles being available at the following locations: Consett, Crook, Durham, Fishburn, Lanchester, Stockton, Washington, Winlaton and Wheatley Hill. Depots without pumps would continue to draw supplies from fire stations or depots of the Highways and Bridges Department.

Radio:

The County Council approved a limited radio-telephone installation, which would be linked to a service for the Highways and Bridges Department. Arrangements were in hand for the installation of 34 mobile sets with static stations to be set up at Tow Law and Warden Law and a reserve station sited at the new Ambulance Headquarters at Durham.

Training:

Following a revision of the National Joint Council Scheme of Working Conditions, relating to first aid qualifications, the County Council resolved that in place of the three yearly refresher course currently undertaken by staff, drivers should be required to pass an examination in first aid every three years. Further consideration was to be given to the question of drivers undertaking a limited amount of specialist training associated with their duties.

The above proposals were a major reorganisation of the service and would inevitably take some considerable time to implement in their entirety. Meanwhile day to day progress on operational issues progressed. Prompted by a Ministry of Health Circular 13/54 dealing with major accidents (a circular resulting from the Harrow disaster), plans were drawn up in collaboration with the police, fire and hospital services to cover these and other major emergencies.

This process continues to this day through the Joint Emergency Liaison Group (JELG). However, back then real progress was made in respect of pre-organised arrangements and contingencies for major civil disasters whereby ambulance services would:

(a) notify prescribed hospitals of the need for mobile surgical teams:
(b) provide a staff officer to co-ordinate the call upon ambulance transport at the site of the accident:
(c) provide transport for the mobile surgical team(s):
(d) provide supplies of spare stretchers, blankets and first aid equipment.

This was a forerunner of modern day Major Incident Plans and the essential elements of this scheme remain valid to this day. Another important development that took place during 1956 was that 30 ambulances were fitted with mobile radios and were reported to be working with increasing efficiency by the end of the year. This experiment continued into 1957 and proved to be extremely successful.

The service once again experienced a slight rise in the total number of patients carried but paradoxically saw for the first time a fall in the miles travelled. Whilst the records do not elaborate why this was so, we might conclude that the decrease was perhaps a reflection on the introduction of more efficient working arrangements! The number of patients carried showed a slight increase of 3,822 (298,612 in total), but the number of miles travelled decreased by 33,769 to 2,253,087.

Although this trend was reversed again in 1955 with 12,576 additional patients being carried (311,188 in total), and the miles travelled going up by 50,226 to 2,303,313. Although the mileage increase was just under 4%, in real terms this was nearly 1,000 miles per week, but this was a national trend caused by the reduction of petrol supplies, followed by rationing as a consequence of the Suez Crisis. Under the guidelines issued by the Ministry of Transport, ambulances were given 'fuel priority', but at the same time there was a relaxation of the criteria on providing outpatient transport in order to reduce the demand on private travel. The problem continued until after the spring, but the then Minister of Transport, Herbert Watkins, issued considerable relaxation on motoring regulations, including raising the speed limit on commercial vehicles. At the same time his colleague, the Minister of Health, gave formal approval to a number of ambulance and fire service re-organisation proposals, including those submitted by Durham County Council.

For the first time the service experienced a fall in demand for its services in 1956 with 306,674 patients carried (-4,514) over 2,259,284 miles (-44,029). Ironically, at the same time the area's main local bus service operator (United Automobile Services) also saw a decline in travelling passengers, but sales of private cars and motorbikes (especially combinations) increased substantially in the northern region.

Above:
The joint Red Cross and St. John Ambulance Committee did a lot of good work for the Durham service. This view shows one of the joint committee's Austin Princess ambulances in 1957.

By the mid-1950s it was becoming evident that new 'light' ambulances would have to be developed to meet the growing demand being placed on ambulance services nationally. To meet this need, especially for outpatient transport, manufacturers took up the challenge. Most notable was Bedford, who developed their CA light van for ambulance use. Several types were evaluated by Durham, including Lever's 'Lancastrian' seen here, but they eventually settled on the CA with a Lomas body.
Courtesy: Vauxhall Motors

During 1957 final preparations were being made for the introduction of re-organisational changes approved by the Minister the previous year and early in 1958 a short report was given to the County Council; reviewing the achievements of the service over its first ten years. The major elements of that report are reproduced here:

'A review of the ambulance service over the past ten years provides a history of sustained effort made to secure a higher standard of efficiency in operating an important public service.

Its most effective contribution, in terms of cases handled, has been in the transport of those members of the public needing outpatient treatment. There has always been reason to believe that hospitals and doctors could exercise more care in requiring the use of ambulance transport, particularly in the case of outpatients, and constant efforts have been maintained, with the help of the Ministry of Health, to persuade them to be more discriminating in this respect. That these efforts are bearing fruit seems to be indicated by the steady reduction in the number of such cases transported over recent years, as shown by the following figures:

Year	No. of out-patient cases transported
1955	227,003
1956	222,379
1957	220,795
1958	218,459

The demand on the service peaked in 1952 and has fluctuated with comparatively slight variation since that year, the principal change being the reduction in the number of outpatients carried since 1956.'

What was not said in the report, is that ever since its inception the service had seen a year upon year rise in demand (with the exception of 1956) and that this general trend had continued despite the recent fall in outpatient activity. It is therefore evident that there was actually a continuing rise in the demand for the emergency services.

This may be confirmed by the fact that during this year the service conveyed some 24,838 emergency patients in comparison to 3,749 in 1949 (an increase of 650% over the first full year of operation). Taking both categories of transport together, almost a quarter of a million patients were carried, well over double the number carried in that first year. In real terms the figures had grown by around 10% per annum in that first decade, a statistic that reflects on the growing expectations of the population from its National Health Service.

As stated earlier, the reorganisation came into effect on 1st April 1958, with the major element being the centralised control facility at Durham Headquarters. The changes made meant a considerable movement of staff around the County to provide the new service with its redesigned format of 24-hour stations and general duty stations providing cover 8am to 8pm Monday to Friday and 8am to 4pm on Saturdays. The facilities used to carry out this service are shown in left-hand column below, whilst the human resource requirements are listed in the right-hand column.

Headquarters control	1	Headquarters staff	16
Agent controls	2	Headquarters control staff:	
Message receiving centres	6	Supervisors	4
Ambulance depots:		Control room assistants	6
24-hour	11	Relief telephonist	2
12 hour	7	Radio operator	1
Ambulances	94	Depot telephonists	5
Light sitting case vehicles	8	Liaison officers	2
Cars	2	Head drivers	14
Breakdown vehicle	1	Mechanics	4
Total Vehicles	**105**	**Total Personnel**	**54**

The 24-hour emergency service was now provided from the six message receiving centres plus the agent controls at Darlington and West Hartlepool, New Herrington Depot, Hartlepool Depot and the out-station on call. A period of consolidation followed although demands on the service continued to rise and by the end of 1962 the service was carrying more than 362,000 patients over almost two and a half million miles a year.

In 1963 Mr Birch, Chief Ambulance Officer, retired and Mr George Dewen was appointed in his place on 14th October. The new Chief Officer presided over yet another review of the ambulance service, completed in early 1964, with the purpose of considering the efficiency of the service, and taking into account-

   (a) the standard of service provided and

   (b) its cost as compared with the cost of services in other comparable counties.

In an attempt to make the review as comprehensive as possible consideration was also given to the following operational factors: -

   (a) i) the adequacy of the number of vehicles

        ii) the appropriate ratio of sitting case vehicles (outpatient) to ambulances (emergency vehicles) and dual purpose vehicles (those suitable for both).

        iii) the most economical use of existing vehicles

        iv) the optimum economical life of vehicles

        v) complaints regarding the inadequacy of heating in ambulances

   b) i) the adequacy in the number of staff, both control and operations, account being taken of recent reduction of work hours per week and the amount of sickness and absenteeism.

        ii) the efficient and economic utilisation of existing staff

        iii) annual overtime costs

        iv) employment of casual drivers

   (c) Staff problems and the adequacy of consultation.

It was recognised that all of these factors were inter-related and that deficiencies in one area could impact on the efficiency of another unrelated area. As a result the Health Committee of the County Council approved the recommendations listed opposite.

Left:
During the 1950s, Durham County Ambulance staff were issued with white dust coats, such as these pictured on the crew members of this Bedford K1 ambulance in its dark green livery.

(1)   That attention be given to re-organising the central control and ensuring the adequacy of control staff.

(2)   To meet, as far as possible, the shortage of staff during summer months, a comprehensive winter training scheme for new recruits should be inaugurated after the 'Ministry of Health Working Party' report on 'Training of Ambulance Personnel' was published. These newly trained personnel would relieve during the summer holiday periods and the normal principle of staggering summer holidays between 1st April and 30th September would be implemented.

(3)   The total number of vehicles would be increased from 120 to 137 with the intention of providing an adequate reserve fleet, allowing replacement for vehicles withdrawn for maintenance and repairs without reducing the total operational fleet.

(4)   The establishment of vehicles be 56 conventional ambulances (emergency), 26 dual-purpose vehicles and 55 light sitting case vehicles (outpatient), and that this number and ratio be reviewed from time to time.

(5)   All vehicles, including senior officers' private cars, to be equipped with radio. The radio equipment, of the frequency modulation (FM) type, to be fitted to all ambulances and dual purpose vehicles in the first instance and then sitting case vehicles at a later date.

(6)   That only petrol-engined ambulances be purchased in future.

(7)   The new conventional ambulances should provide maximum comfort for stretcher cases and that separate heaters be installed in the rear cabs of all the vehicles.

(8)   That a policy of renewing vehicles at regular specific intervals, previously suggested, should be introduced. This system of planned replacement thus enabling a forward purchasing plan to be introduced and avoid the difficulties previously experienced by late deliveries of new vehicles and frequent break-downs of old vehicles.

(9)   The possibility of distributing emergency vehicles over more depots during the day and night rather than concentrating them in a smaller number of depots should be explored after an accurate, effective and meticulous control system and wireless control was operating.

(10) That the hospital and GPs be asked to co-operate as far as possible to give the service 24-hours notice of non-emergency transport requests so that these journeys could be planned and co-ordinated.

(11) The possibility of installing closed-circuit teleprinter equipment be considered in the near future.

The aforementioned proposals were a considerable change in ambulance provision, but change was inevitable in order to meet the demand as yet again the service saw a further rise in its statistics with 383,369 patients (+21,366) being carried 2,554,115 miles (+105,983). It was recognised that it would take some time to fully implement the above changes. Yet, some aspects were more visible, and there came the introduction of a new image for the service with new vehicles and uniform for the staff.

The installation of new radios commenced during the year and more centralisation of the control system took place. Early in 1965 plans were drawn up for a much needed new building to house the central control in order to relieve the congestion being experienced at Ambulance HQ. In 1966 some radical changes were approved for implementation early in 1967 in line with the review carried out during 1963. The major change was that all ambulance depots would go onto 24-hour working and therefore provide emergency services from every site. Work commenced on the new control building, but as far as the crews were concerned the big change was a further reduction in the working week to 40 hours.

The reduction in working hours was some compensation, but it was still a hard physical job, and some crews faced even more hazardous duties. For example the service continued to be responsible for conveying all the cases of smallpox and suspected smallpox in the geographical counties of Cumberland, Northumberland and Durham and also in parts of Westmorland and the North Riding of Yorkshire. The reason for this wide area of coverage was that the smallpox hospital for these areas was situated at Langley Park. Following the outbreak of a smallpox epidemic in the West Riding of Yorkshire in 1962, members of staff were given vaccinations and issued with protective clothing. Fortunately, Durham was not affected by this epidemic but the experience was valuable and thereafter all drivers were offered re-vaccination against smallpox. Annual arrangements were made for the 'vaccine protected' drivers to visit Langley Park Hospital, where training was given in the practice and procedures for the carrying and handling of smallpox cases.

During 1967, for the first time, a cost was reported for the running of the ambulance service. It was identified that the Ambulance Service and the Home Help Service were the two most expensive services provided by the Health Department in County Durham with the Ambulance Service costing £620,000 in this year. This compares with the cost 30 years on of more than £8 million in 1997. The first experience of industrial action was encountered in 1967 when drivers at two depots took action over separate issues. At Stockton, drivers refused to convey out-patients as they disputed the continued use of casual labour and at Hebburn drivers refused to be available for work on rest and free days, the cause being the order of calling in personnel for such overtime work. The first issue was taken up by one of the unions, which resulted in a representation being made to ambulance headquarters to say that in future permanent staff would not work with casual labour. Arrangements were commenced therefore, to obtain permanent relief drivers for future years. The second dispute was resolved locally.

Despite these problems the demand for transport continued at a high level with 402,563 patients carried over 2,696,792 miles. In 1968, there was a substantial reduction in the Durham figures because of the transfer of the Stockton depot to the newly formed Teesside Borough Council. Effective from 1st April 1968, this transfer resulted in the transfer of nine vehicles and a number of staff. As a direct consequence of this the number of patients carried by Durham County Ambulance Service during the year reduced to 363,990, whilst the vehicles operating from 17 depots covered 2,467,313 miles. Yet despite the transfer of vehicles and staff out of the Durham service, at the end of the year it employed a total of 352 staff and 135 ambulances.

The development of modern technology continued, especially with respect to communications. Telex machines were installed at Headquarters and nine depots to allow for the passing of work directly to these depots, while work was commenced on an improved telephone system. While the costs of providing the service rose to almost £750,000 in 1970, not every aspect of the operation was running smoothly. Changes were required and the use of computer technology was proposed as a means of providing continuous statistical analysis of the emergency ambulance demand patterns. The idea behind this was to use this data to model the provision of services in the future, but the plans were shelved as staff were unwilling to co-operate in making the changes required to the way in which records were compiled. This stance by the staff was a reaction to the lack of progress in the implementation of a productivity scheme. Although the real problem was not one of willingness to implement a scheme, but rather the difficulty in deciding how productivity could be reasonably and accurately measured within the ambulance service.

Left:

Prior to the 1960s, the service had no formal uniform for its staff, so a variety of 'informal' work-clothes were worn, as demonstrated in this 1948 picture. Later staff would be issued with uniforms, and each man was entitled to one jacket, two pairs of trousers, greatcoat, cap (with covers) and two dustcoats. Courtesy Enid Walton

Right:

In 1964 uniforms with appropriate rank markings were duly issued to the six senior officers in post, namely Mr G C Dewen, Mr A Barrass, Mr E Kent, Mr B Middlewood, Mr W White and Mr W McAdam, with other grades getting their's soon after. Also, following a demonstration of vehicles by various manufacturers it was decided to change the type and colour of ambulance vehicles. This saw the livery changing from a very dark green colour to a cream (called Harvest Gold) body with a brown stripe at the waistband, whilst the service decided to concentrate its main purchases of ambulances on Austin LD chassis fitted with Wadham bodies. All these changes are demonstrated to good effect in this 1966 view at Framwellgate Moor. With (from left to right) Bert Middlewood (station officer), Bill McAdam (Staff Officer - Control & Communications), Isaac Barras (Deputy Chief Ambulance Officer and George Dewen (Chief Ambulance Officer).

Industrial relations were further soured on two more occasions during 1970 when ambulancemen refused to carry out their full range of duties because of disputes at local and national level. On the first occasion the dispute was in connection with the alleged delay by the County Council in the implementation of the previously mentioned productivity scheme. The second dispute was in support of a national scheme for an increase in wage rates. Even so, in both instances staff continued to operate an emergency service. Demands for transport continued to rise during 1970, and despite the industrial problems some 383,135 patients were carried over 2,615,235 miles.

Technological advances continued, but they did not come without their complications however and during 1971, as the control centre at Durham adopted more and more telecommunications equipment, concerns grew regarding the vulnerability to power failure. In consequence provision was made during the year for a 7Kva alternator associated with the Health Department's Mobile Dental Unit to be parked at the control. In the event of mains supply disruption, this emergency system would provide an auxiliary circuit supplying sufficient power to operate modified lighting, one telex machine and the stand-by radio transmitter. For longer-term interruptions the service planned to use an externally sourced 35Kva alternator which supplied sufficient power to operate all systems normally.

During this year the Durham service was chosen to participate in the testing of a system of control procedure devised by the Ambulance Service Advisory Committee and the Chief Ambulance Officer attended preliminary discussions on this project.

The control centre was continuing to develop technologically during 1972, with a 9-exchange line PABX switchboard being installed. A direct line was also provided to Dryburn Hospital along with an 'out of area line' to Bishop Auckland. There were additional direct lines to both police and fire controls independent of the switchboard. Furthermore, by the end of the 1960s, it was appreciated that the existing radio equipment would have to be replaced by a more sophisticated short-wave system.

Table 4: Resources 1964

Many changes had taken place to the infrastructure over the years, and it is worth recording where the 19 vehicle depots were on 31st December 1964.

Depot	Staff	Vehicles
Barnard Castle	2	1
Bishop Auckland	30	9
Chester-le-Street	12	6
Consett	12	6
Crook	8	6
Durham	40	14
Fishburn	10	6
Hartlepool	5	1
Hebburn	30	10
Houghton le Spring	24	6
Middleton-in-Teesdale	2	1
Newton Aycliffe	2	1
Seaham	8	4
Stanley	28	8
St Johns Chapel	2	1
Stockton	29	10
Washington	7	5
Wheatley Hill	32	11
Winlaton	9	5
Totals	**292**	**111**

Above:
The first primitive radio system at the Durham HQ with two microphones and two tranceivers. One was devoted to the transmitter at Tow Law, the other to the mast at Warden Law (interestingly the name Law is derived from the old English word Hlaw, meaning high burial place).

Below:
Operating through four transmitter sites the replacement system covered the entire county along with North Yorkshire and used data transmission rather than vocal communication, although a facility for voice communication was included in the equipment. Durham County was the first ambulance service to order such equipment and this is essentially what is currently used in the service today.

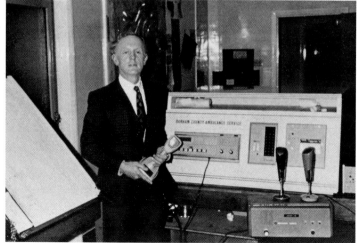

It was expected that the new radio equipment, to be supplied by Motorola, would be fully operational by mid-1973. The use of this equipment would bring to an end the rather novel radio procedure previously in use. Until this time all the depots were named after birds with the main depots named after birds beginning with the letter 'p', e.g. peacock, pigeon and partridge. At times this could be confusing for the radio operators, but with practice on the system it usually resulted in reasonably efficient working. However, the new system using data transmission would mean that each ambulance would be designated a 3-figure code, which would become its radio call sign.

Demand for transport rose yet again in 1973 with the service seeing over 400,000 patients for the first time since Stockton had transferred out of the County to Stockton Borough Council in 1968. Some 418,970 patients travelled 2,792,807 miles, but this was a 'swan-song' for 1973 was the final year of County Council administration of the Durham County Ambulance Service. With effect from the 1st April 1974 the service was to be administered by the Health Authority, so progress in this final year before change was therefore not surprisingly sluggish.

The major event of the year was the first all out strike of ambulance operational staff, which occurred in November when depot personnel instituted a strike because it had not been possible to introduce the productivity bonus scheme. This industrial action lasted four days after which time the staff returned to duty but refused to convey anyone other than emergency patients. Further consideration was given by the service management to the institution of a productivity scheme and at the end of the year such a scheme was evolved by the Management Services Unit of the County Council and was put to staff for their consideration.

The biggest change of all would come with an alteration in the County's geography in 1974, when boundary changes would substantially reduce the size of the operational area. This meant that several ambulance stations would be transferred to the new authorities, including the depots at Hebburn, New Herrington, Washington and Winlaton, all of which became part of the newly formed Northumbria Ambulance Service (which served Tyne & Wear and Northumberland). But, County Durham did gain Darlington which had lost its County Borough status under the boundary changes. This meant that the new Health Authority ambulance service described in the following section would comprise 14 depots at: -

Barnard Castle	Fishburn
Bishop Auckland	Middleton-in-Teesdale
Chester-le-Street	Newton Aycliffe
Consett	Seaham
Crook	Stanley
Darlington	St Johns Chapel
Durham	Wheatley Hill

Except for the above little else was achieved in the last year other than to make the necessary arrangements for the 'hand over' of administrative control.

Staff and Estates

The end of 1949 saw the number of depots reduced from 42 to 24, but it was still proving difficult to provide better accommodation for driving staff. It was recognised that much of the existing accommodation was inadequate, with many vehicles having to stand outside in the open. A special sub-committee was appointed to inspect depots, potential sites and new buildings in the hope that progress could be made. The number of driver-attendants employed at the end of the year was 248 (130 more than the previous year) and efforts continued to increase this to the establishment level of 263.

Above:
Durham Ambulance Station, with a member of staff washing a Wadham-bodied Austin LD ambulance c1965.   Courtesy: Ron Henderson

Wage rates were agreed nationally through The National Working Conditions for ambulance drivers, prescribed by the National Joint Industrial Council of Local Authorities' Non-Trading Services (Manual Workers). At the end of the year 136 drivers were in receipt of a wage exceeding the national agreement rate, while 109 were receiving the wage council rate of £5 13s 0d (£5.65p), the remaining three drivers being employed by the three agencies. Drivers and attendants with a certificate in first aid, which was recognised by the appropriate Provincial Council, received an extra 6s (30p) per week (effective from the 25th June 1949) in recognition of that qualification. In addition, head drivers who supervised staff at a station received the following additional weekly sums:

In charge of 4 or less ambulances	8s 0d (40p)
In charge of 5 and up to 8 ambulances	11s 0d (55p)
In charge of more than 8 ambulances	14s 0d (70p)

Above:
Darlington's ambulance station remained in the old fire brigade premises for many years, and this Leyland EA with a Wadham body is seen outside in 1972. Contrast this picture with that of the horse-ambulance leaving the same building which is seen on page 2. Courtesy: R. Henderson

Manpower was again increased through 1950 to help deal with the increases in demands on the service and at the year end there were 268 driver-attendants in post, up 20 on the previous year and it had been agreed to increase the establishment to 286. One driver was placed at the Royal Victoria Infirmary in Newcastle, to act as a liaison officer in an effort to achieve some economy of expenditure in this area. Little movement was made in the building of new depots, but some progress was made in other accommodation areas.

The depot numbers were reduced to 19, made up of 15 principal depots, one small coastal depot and three out-stations covering the rural areas of Weardale and Teesdale. Premises for adaptation were purchased at Wheatley Hill, Bishop Auckland and Stanley, while new sites were identified at Chester-le-Street and New Herington. More suitable garage premises had meanwhile been rented for the vehicles at Crook, St. Johns Chapel and South Cleatlam, near Barnard Castle.

During 1951 an application was submitted from the unions to the effect that ambulance-driving staff should be considered as 'shift workers'. Following a meeting on 7th September 1951 a compromise was reached whereby workers would relinquish their claim to a shift allowance in return for the payment of 4/7d (23p) per week backdated to 1st April 1950, as a 'plus payment' while engaged on rota work. The number of driving staff increased again to 270, an increase of only two and still short of the agreed establishment level of 286.

During the following year, 1952, the number of operational staff increased by only a single person, although headquarters staff increased to a total of 13 including the appointment of two liaison officers to act in the Service's interests at Newcastle and Sunderland hospitals. Depots at Stanley, Consett and Bishop Auckland were improved and tenders accepted for the building of new depots at Chester-le-Street and New Herrington. Construction work was soon under way at both places and plans were drawn up for new depots at Crook, Durham, Sedgefield, Stockton and Washington. Bishop Auckland Depot moved into newly converted premises at South Church.

By 1953, both Chester-le Street and New Herrington depots were completed and they came into operation on 14th May and 27th June respectively, while new building work was commenced at Crook,

Fishburn, Stockton and Washington, as well as a new combined depot and HQ at Durham. A garage extension was also undertaken at Stanley.

However, crew numbers stayed almost static with only one additional driver being employed, although headquarters staff numbers were increased with the appointment of two staff officers. The six mechanics approved in the previous year were also in position and operating from the identified maintenance depots. Consequential of the 1954 review, changes in depot-manning were undertaken, including the classification of the out-stations and New Herrington, Hartlepool and Durham depots as message receiving centres providing a 24-hour service. The remaining seven depots would work 12-hour long 'day' shifts only to meet local needs. Also proposed was the closure of the Lanchester depot, with its staff and vehicles moving to Durham on 31st December 1955.

Additionally there were extensive proposals, described earlier, for the provision of petrol and fuel supplies at many depots throughout the County. New depots came into use at Washington and Stockton on 3rd February and 26th April 1954 respectively, while good progress was reported at Winlaton and on the new headquarters building and depot at Durham. This would open on 28th March 1955, and the headquarters of the service would remain at this site until the present day. New depots were also scheduled for Hartlepool, Seaham and Hebburn, but work had not yet commenced.

The Minister of Health approved further staff increases during 1955 to assist with the growing demand, allowing the service to employ 293 operational staff. Even so only 272 driver-attendants were in post by the end of the year, and this was actually a decrease of nine staff on the previous year. By 1956 the number of stations had been rationalised to 15 plus three out-stations. Twenty-four hour cover was provided from the six message receiving centres shown in the table (right) as well as from the three out-stations at Middleton-in-Teesdale, South Cleatlam and St.Johns Chapel who provided an emergency service at nights on an 'On Call' basis. Additional 24-hour cover was provided by the West Hartlepool and Darlington services. All other stations were providing 12-hour cover only.

Table 5: Message Receiving Centres and Stations 31st December 1956

MESSAGE RECEIVING CENTRES	AMBULANCE STATIONS
Ambulance Station 1, St Johns Avenue Hebburn (Tel: Hebburn 32157)	(1) 1 St Johns Avenue, Hebburn (2) Hostel Estate, Washington
Ambulance Station East Street Stanley (Tel: Stanley 392)	(1) Knowledge Hill, Winlaton (2) East Street, Stanley (3) Villa Real, Consett
Ambulance Station Byron Street Wheatley Hill (Tel: Thornley 243)	(1) Byron Street, Wheatley Hill (2) Bankhead Street, Seaham (3) Back Raglan Row, Philadelphia, Houghton-le-Spring
Ambulance Station Grangefield Road Stockton-on-Tees (Tel: Stockton 67410)	(1) Grangefield Road, Stockton-on-Tees
Ambulance Station South Church Road Bishop Auckland (Tel: Bishop Auckland 810)	(1) South Church Road, B/p Auckland (2) 19 South Cleatlam, Winston (3) Alston Road Garage, Middleton-in-Teesdale (4) Near Roddymoor Road Ends, Crook (5) St. Johns Chapel, Weardale
Ambulance Headquarters Finchale Road Framwellgate Moor Durham (Tel: Durham 3587)	(1) Framwellgate Moor, Durham (2) Elderberry Bank, Fishburn (3) Osborne Road, Chester-le-Street

Left:

There is an old saying in the ambulance service, 'that you shouldn't have joined if you can't take a joke', but some members of the Durham Service had a more virile sense of humour than others. This is shown by a cartoon drawn by Ivor Thornton, which depicts Joe Coxon (control room clerk) and Bill Elgey (telephone operator) in the early 1970s. This was at a time when staff were trying for increased wages under the then Public Sector pay constraints that had been introduced by the new Conservative Government. Unable to get anywhere at No.10, the characters try for a handout from the former Prime Minister Harold Wilson.

Above:
In rural parts of Durham, crews often had to face atrocious driving conditions. This is shown by this very poor photograph from the winter of 1973, which (although lacking in technical quality) reveals the hazards faced by John Snow and his partner whilst going from Bishop Auckland to an urgent maternity case at Evenwood

During 1957 staff continued to make representations through the unions to be recognised as shift workers and remunerated accordingly. As a result the 'inconvenient working hours' payment was increased by two and a half old pence (1p) per hour with effect from 2nd August. A dispute with the trade unions arose during the year after concern was expressed about the servicing of vehicles; although this was described in the CMO's report as a difference of opinion, it had not been resolved by the end of the year.

New depots were opened at Hartlepool and Seaham on the 30th July 1957 and 12th August 1957 respectively. Meanwhile the numbers of staff continued to fluctuate, never reaching the approved establishment. By 1960 the new depot at Hebburn entered operational service on 7th January, whilst proposals for a new station at Bishop Auckland received attention, as did similar plans for the re-siting of the South Cleatlam outstation to Barnard Castle.

A site was also earmarked for the building of what was described as an 'outstation' at Newton Aycliffe. Today this is one of the major stations within the present county but, back then, Newton Aycliffe was in its infancy as a 'New Town' and the proposals for any ambulance presence at all was a plan for the future rather than a measure to meet existing need.

With effect from the 1st April 1960 Head Drivers were re-designated as Depot Superintendents and Senior Drivers were appointed at each depot to act as shift leaders. Wheatley Hill ceased to operate as a message receiving centre with all of its calls now being taken by central control, but the depot itself continued to be operated on a 24-hour basis as an emergency vehicle base.

Work was progressing on the building at Barnard Castle and in the interim the vehicle from South Cleatlam was transferred into temporary garage accommodation within the town. Negotiations were still taking place regarding a new depot at Bishop Auckland and for the procurement of a site for a new out-station at Middleton-in-Teesdale. During 1963 the new out-station at Newton Aycliffe opened for operational duty, and changes were made to the message receiving systems with the transfer to central control of the message receiving functions of both Hebburn and Stanley. They both remained as 24-hour depots providing emergency ambulance services.

Staff had an improvement in their working conditions with a negotiated reduction in the working week from 44 to 42 hours, however, wages were to be paid one week in arrears to bring them into line with council wage payment procedures. The pay scale used to negotiate staff wages during this period was the same as those for other manual workers within council employment i.e. refuse collectors', street sweepers etc. Casual members of staff were employed during the holiday period to provide temporary driver-attendants and arrangements were put in place to train civilian personnel in Civil Defence ambulance duties. To this date all staff had worn largely informal uniforms, but from 1963 proper uniforms with appropriate rank markings had been issued to the six senior officers in post and it was the intention that all staff be issued with formal tunics.

In 1965 plans were prepared for a new, purpose-built central control on the headquarters site. Work actually commenced in 1966, and was completed before the year was out. As mentioned earlier, it was during 1967 that industrial action was experienced for the first time in the service when drivers at Hebburn and Stockton went into dispute. The union supported the more serious Stockton dispute over the employment of casual staff, and as a result arrangements were made to obtain permanent relief drivers for future years. Consequently, by 1968 the service had taken on some 20 additional drivers, although casual staff had still to be employed to cover the service at peak holiday periods.

The CMO's Report submitted to the County Council in 1970 for the first time referred to staff as ambulancemen and not driver-attendants. Now that all new recruits were taking a six-week ambulance aid course at Cleckheaton, this was recognition of their newly earned professional status. A feature of 1971 staffing levels was the low response experienced to advertisements for ambulancemen, which appeared to conflict with the current level of unemployment in the area. This made it very difficult for the service to maintain the level of selectivity necessary to meet the standards needed for post entry training. Yet there was no obvious reason for any reluctance by anyone, to be employed by the ambulance service.

Building work on a new depot at Consett was nearing completion by the end of 1971 whilst approval was given for the construction of a new depot at Stanley to replace the premises which had been adapted in 1950. Outline approval was also given for the construction of a new depot at Peterlee in 1972/73 to replace the adapted Wheatley Hill premises first used in 1949. This final depot would complete the long-term plan of purpose built depots throughout the county.

Fleet and Vehicle Equipment

From the total establishment of 72 vehicles at the end of 1948, progress was made to secure more ambulances, provide better accommodation for staff and vehicles and to recruit additional drivers during 1949. The agency agreement with Chester-le-Street Motor Ambulance Committee was terminated on 30th September 1949 leaving only three agencies within the scheme, and the purchase of all of the vehicles belonging to the voluntary organisations had been completed. The number of vehicles had increased to 92 with 3 cars and 31 new or reconditioned ambulances and 11 old vehicles being declared unserviceable. The new ambulances were either Karrier (13.9 hp) with Lomas bodies or Bedford (27hp) K type with Spurling bodies. During 1950, 22 of the older ambulances were declared unserviceable and 16 new vehicles were delivered. This meant that the fleet size at the end of the year was 86.

From the 1st September 1951 some specialist ambulance duties were identified and, as a result, men from the Lanchester Depot (using five Humber Super Snipe ambulances with Lomas bodies and a Daimler Super Six) undertook all long distance journeys. During this year 20 new Bedford K type ambulances were delivered (again with Lomas bodies) and seven old vehicles taken out of service making 99 ambulances and two cars as the operational fleet. However, one major improvement, which occurred in 1952, was the approval of an establishment of six mechanics for repairs to ambulances at four identified repair units at Crook, Durham, Stanley and Wheatley Hill. A breakdown vehicle was also purchased. An arrangement was then made for major repairs such as re-bores, regrinding of crankshafts and body repairs etc. to be carried out at the County Council's Highways and Bridges Department.

Seventeen more K type ambulances were delivered during 1952 but with 23 ambulances taken out of service the fleet was reduced to 93 plus two cars. It was identified that the rises in demand over recent years had caused problems due to the shortage of vehicles to meet that demand.

The original proposals to provide up to 20 cars to supplement the establishment of 95 ambulances had never been exploited because in practical terms it had been found that cars were too restrictive in the type of patients that they could carry. To resolve this matter the service decided to take advantage of new smaller-powered 'light transit ambulances' and it was intended to acquire eight of these based on the Bedford CA chassis during the following year.

Additionally application had been made to increase the ambulance establishment by 20 ambulances to 115. In the same report it was identified that 30% of the fleet was still stabled outside because of unsatisfactory garage accommodation. In response to this application the Minister of Health approved an increase in the Fleet to 100 vehicles in 1953 and provision was made in the annual estimates of this year for the purchase of the eight light sitting case ambulances. However, the number of ambulances in service actually continued to fall with 91 in service at the end of 1953. During the year 17 more had been purchased but 19 others were taken out of service due to poor condition.

Above:
As Durham standardised its fleet to meet the post-war situation, it turned to Bedford Motors of Luton, who gave the County Council adequate evidence that the Bedford K1 chassis could meet the needs of both town and country driving conditions. One of the first Bedford K1s to be delivered in the northern region was this ambulance supplied to the North Yorkshire Riding service. Representatives of Durham, Northumberland and Westmorland county councils all attended this demonstration of the K1 at Chop Yat in 1949. Quite by coincidence, the Chief Ambulance Officer of the North Riding at this time was a Mr. Bedford!

Below:
To date we have found no photographs of the second generation of post-war Bedford's that Durham employed. This example of a Bedford A2Z was used by Brighton Borough Council, but it is representative of the type of chassis that the Durham service used.
Both Courtesy Vauxhall Motors

Left:
The change from Bedford to Austin/Morris (British Motor Corporation) in the mid-1960s, saw the introduction of lighter bodies. This model dates from 1969 and carries the BMC badge, but it is photographed after transfer to the Northumbria service. Courtesy: Ron Henderson

Centre:
Bearing the appropriate registration plate YHN 999H, this 1970 BMC emergency ambulance shows the type of vehicles used by Darlington Borough and transferred to Durham in 1974. This type was not purchased by the county who were then taking delivery of the British Leyland EA with the Wadham series VIII body. Courtesy: Ron Henderson

Below:
A 'one-off' purchase from the British Leyland stable in 1972, was this Leyland bus. This was used for outpatient travel and had rear doors which gave access to a tail-lift for wheelchair passengers. The regular driver was Bill 'The Bus' Allan, who is seen with his charge, which was No.535 in the fleet.

During 1954, however, the fleet finally increased to 100 ambulances with 12 new vehicles being delivered and only three being withdrawn from service. A further addition to the fleet were the three new light sitting car vehicles. In 1957 the Council's Health Committee purchased nine new Bedford A2Z chassis, again fitting them with Lomas bodies, and then placed orders for a further 11 (four petrol and seven diesel powered). This was the first time that diesel powered vehicles had been considered and the seven ordered were to be tested at suitable locations throughout the county. This was an experiment to determine whether such vehicles could be employed effectively as part of the ambulance fleet, and the 1958 totals include the seven diesels ordered the previous year.

The evaluation must have proved an initial success as a further two were to be ordered in the coming year, but these under-powered and smelly vehicles were not remembered fondly by staff at the time. Harry Cook, who joined the service in 1954 when the Durham Station was at the Gate House in Dryburn Hospital and left in 1986, as the Durham Station Officer (after yet another reorganisation) remembers the introduction of diesel-powered vehicles well. He says ' These vehicles were, in my opinion, a waste of money! The noise of the engines would wake patients up when they drove around the hospitals at night. Apart from the noise, the smell of diesel fuel was all around the vehicle and the heating in the saloon was useless. Vibration was also a problem, top speed on the main roads could be 45 to 50 mph with a tail wind. The diesel ambulances at that time were an embarrassment to ambulancemen.' In contrast Harry remembers the main fleet of 28hp Bedford K1's fondly, by saying that 'they gave wonderful service for many years.'

It would not be long before the idea of diesel ambulances was shelved and no more purchased. Petrol vehicles were ultimately found to be much more user friendly for patients and staff as diesel fuel was still very unrefined and at this time almost exclusively limited to use by larger commercial vehicles.

By way of contrast 1960 was a good year for the fleet with ten light sitting case Austin JU 250's with Kenning bodies and ten Bedford CA's with Lomas bodies put into service, with orders placed for a further ten ambulances and 18 sitting case vehicles. A considerable part of the review of the ambulance service instigated by Mr Dewen in 1963 related to the fleet size, its composition, design and equipment. After all, as a transport organisation, which is what the ambulance service was viewed as in these days, the nature and competence of its fleet was central to its business. The specific areas covered by the report are mentioned elsewhere, but its final part deserves emphasis for it was at this time that the livery changed from the green colour to cream with the reddish/brown stripe. These changes were brought into effect during 1964 when nine new ambulances were delivered in the new livery and orders were placed for 32 more.

By 1965 the fleet size had finally increased sufficiently to allow a pool of reserve vehicles to be established. This meant that there were now sufficient ambulances in the fleet to allow small numbers of vehicles to be taken out of service for maintenance or repair without disrupting work schedules for the carriage of patients. It had taken 17 years of planned investment to reach this stage, but it would be the model for future fleet provision. The fleet now numbered 130 ambulances, of which 117 were conventional ambulances and 13 were light sitting case vehicles.

This reasonably satisfactory position continued until 1972 when difficulties were encountered from the suppliers who were then facing an upturn in demand at a time of severe steel (and other material) shortages. The service had, at this time, some 79 vehicles on order, made up of 32 conventional emergency type ambulances and 47 dual-purpose vehicles. As a consequence of these difficulties some of the older Austin LD's with Wadham bodies, which had been due for disposal, had to be retained for at least a further two years until the replacements arrived. This situation had not improved by the time the service underwent re-organisation in 1974.

Above: *Class 2 of 1973 at the North East Ambulance Training Centre*

Training and Ambulance Care Equipment

Other than the desirability of having a first aid certificate there were no training requirements in the early days of the service and even this was not mandatory. In fact any member of staff who was willing to obtain a recognised certificate received extra pay. This situation continued until 1954 when as part of the review of that year the Council resolved that each driver should be required to pass an examination in first aid every three years. This was the first time ambulance staff had been required to undergo any such examination process. In addition there was a suggestion that ambulance drivers could take a limited amount of special training.

In 1962 there were some significant developments including the Smallpox training and the introduction of 'Porton' resuscitators on those ambulances scheduled for emergency duties. The vehicles were also fitted with blue all-round flashing lights at the same time. These measures were in response to a Ministry of Health circular and were an important step forward in patient care capability. The resuscitator provided had a bellows and facemask designed to emulate the breathing of a patient who suffered respiratory arrest. Then, in 1969 a number of significant local and national developments took place. The major change was the introduction of training both on a national/regional basis and a local basis. Six-week ambulance aid courses for ambulance staff were introduced and courses were held at Birmingham and Cleckheaton. Only new recruits to the service were required to complete these courses, because those members of staff already employed and experienced were given exemption.

In addition a new North East Training School, operated by a consortium of authorities in the region opened in temporary premises at the Newcastle Ambulance Service Headquarters. This was later to transfer to Tynemouth, where courses were held for supervisory staff and 'refresher training' given to ambulancemen with two to five years service. Staff from the service had during this period attended a variety of training courses both at Cleckheaton and Tynemouth, and in total 87 people attended these courses, 31 going on the 6 week ambulance aid courses and 58 taking the 2 week refresher courses. Then in 1972 further developments took place with the purchase of 'Scoop Stretchers'. These were used in the movement of patients suffering orthopaedic injury and to minimise the movement necessary to a casualty in order to load them onto the lifting surface. In addition ambulance trolleys were now replacing stretchers when new vehicles were being brought into the service.

Despite the increased levels of training the equipment provided to ambulance staff had changed little over the years until 1971. This was an important year for Durham County Ambulance Service. It saw the introduction of some major items of equipment, which would significantly enhance the care given to patients. This equipment included oxygen driven resuscitators, electric suction units manufactured by Laerdal, bag and mask manual resuscitators made by Airox, a portable analgesic (painkilling) set consisting of 'Entonox', a gas mixture of oxygen and nitrous oxide, sets of inflatable splints and spinal splints. Training arrangements with respect to this equipment were given to all the staff.

The First Twenty Five Years - A Conclusion

The first 25 years had proved to be a period of considerable change, and only hindsight can show how great these changes were. We can only guess how many lives they saved, and how important these changes were in the transport of sick and injured to and from hospital. The big changes had been in the infrastructure of the unwieldy and largely haphazard service that had commenced with 42 depots and nine control centres, but finished with one highly efficient control centre managing 17 depots.

Slow progress had been made in improving patient care, but this was not because the ambulance services did not recognise the need. Rather it was a matter of more pressing problems and in the later years this aspect had obviously improved, as it became more of a focus. Public funding (and the overall public concept of the ambulance service) was still geared to a transport service, rather than an actual provider of pre-hospital and emergency care. However, the major steps forward in this area were yet to be seen and would not materialise for some time. Yet change was coming, and not just for the Durham service. To create a more effective national ambulance service, the Ministry of Health had commissioned the Miller Report. In his book *NHS Ambulances - The First 25 Years*, Chris Batten records this milestone event, stating:'It was another important stage in development, in that it took account of the views of doctors, hospitals and ambulance crews. It was published in two parts, the first recommended having basic standards of training for ambulance personnel, whilst the second dealt with the equipment to be carried by ambulances. Prior to this there was an uncoordinated approach with individual services [including Durham] deciding their own standard of service, vehicles and equipment.' There was thus a new era of thinking coming forward, and at last forethought was being put into the provision of new services, and also the crews and vehicles that were required to operate them.

Part of this philosophy would impact on the ambulance manufacturers, with significant changes being introduced and many old makers going out of business. Dennis Brothers of Guildford, today better known for their fire engines, lead the way with a new style prototype ambulance. This vehicle, the FD4 had its genesis in the Miller Report, however it was not a commercial success and it never went into full production.

On the other hand Bedford and Ford were both to introduce chassis-cab models of their standard commercial vans on to which fibreglass ambulance bodies could be mounted. It was the introduction of these lighter, faster ambulances that would allow for the carriage of more and more life-saving equipment. The introduction of this equipment in turn spurred on the training of its use by ambulance personnel. It was just part of the progress of change, but it was to be of untold value to those people for who the service was summoned by dialling 999!

Left:
The last of the heavy ambulances purchased by Durham County Council was a batch of 56 Leyland EA chassis with Wadham Series VIII bodies in 1972. Two types of body were obtained for the EA chassis, each reflecting the type of duties to be performed as the ambulance service became tiered into emergency or outpatient transport. The example seen left is one of the outpatient vehicles, a fact that can be readily determined by the clear glass windows fitted to the saloon of the vehicle. The example seen here is photographed in the livery of the Northumbria Service, having been transferred after the boundary changes of 1974.
Courtesy: Ron Henderson

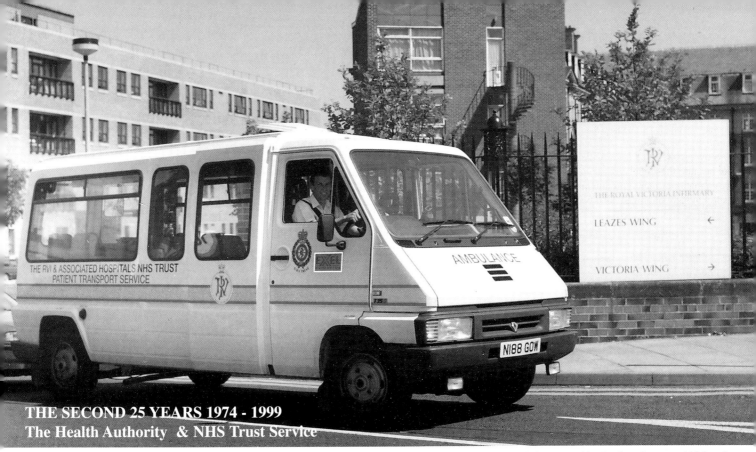

THE SECOND 25 YEARS 1974 - 1999
The Health Authority & NHS Trust Service

With the boundary changes of 1974 the towns of Hartlepool, Stockton and their surrounds were all transferred to Cleveland, whilst areas south of the Tyne including Sunderland, Washington, Hebburn, Houghton, Herrington and Winlaton all moved out of County Durham and into the new Tyne & Wear Metropolitan area.

It was a much smaller geographic area that the new Durham ambulance service would cover thereafter (although it now included the Darlington Borough Council area), but there were other significant changes too. Perhaps the biggest changes came within the area's traditional industries, although there were also important moves to improve housing.

Central to both of these issues were the changes in the coal mining industry, as the NCB began to close many of the smaller (less efficient) pits and quite a number of the larger ones that were officially classed as 'worked out'.

In the Durham Dales, traditional industries like farming and quarrying were facing hard times as mechanisation reduced the numbers employed. Lead mining, which had employed tens of thousands at the start of the century, had all but vanished. In Darlington the heavy engineering industry was in decline, and the closure of the huge British Railway workshops and the English Electric plant were huge blows to the town.

Above: A *Renault Master Ambulance used by Durham between 1996 and 1999 as part of the Royal Victoria Infirmary contract in Newcastle.*

Squalid housing, erected by the old private mining companies and some industrial firms, which were substandard even by Victorian standards, required demolition to provide modern houses with adequate facilities. Durham County Council undertook a large programme of housing renewal, but many properties were fit only for demolition. The village of Witton Park near Bishop Auckland was a classic example, but it was never completely cleared and it duly featured in a Granada television programme entitled 'The Village That Refused To Die'.

Elsewhere 'new towns', like Peterlee and Newton Aycliffe were developed, whilst many existing towns were redeveloped with modern shopping precincts in their central areas and new housing estates on their fringe. It all meant a major change in the way ambulance services were going to be delivered, and as a consequence some redeployment accompanied the planning of the service. Following the re-organisation and the change into Health Authority management control, the staff and management of the ambulance service were viewed as a part of the healthcare network for the first time.

Organisation, Management and Demand

The aforementioned changes would ultimately lead to the expansion of the ambulance service, and a much higher profile was accorded to its staff and the skills they displayed. As part of the new arrangements, and in line with Miller Report recommendations, a central control was very much part of the service now. Accordingly hospitals throughout the region were asked to ensure that requests for all ambulance transport were directed through central control so that services could be co-ordinated on a county-wide basis.

The new radio system, which had been installed using Motorola equipment in 1973, now allowed the central control to contact vehicles while mobile, in order to allocate additional work or to advise changes in their planned duties. A limited system of data transmission was also allowed under this radio system with crews sending numerical codes to control over the radio to signify their present status. For instance crews were instructed that when leaving a hospital with patients going home they should first enter the number code of the hospital (e.g. 19 for Dryburn hospital in Durham) followed by code 37 to indicate that this was a return journey with patients on board. These numerical codes were entered by a crew-member pressing numbered buttons on the radio set in the ambulance cab. Despite this efficient system some hospitals continued to by-pass central control and called local depots to order ambulances for patients. What is more, some of the Depot Superintendents continued to accept these calls and despatch ambulances locally. This obviously reduced the level of central control and therefore the effectiveness of the service. As a result on 5th June 1974 Mr Dewen, the Chief Ambulance Officer, had to remind all Superintendents that this practice had to stop and all such calls should thereafter be redirected to central control.

The major change that resulted from the ambulance service transfer into Health Authority responsibility was that a much greater emphasis would now be placed on patient care, training and sharing of best practice, not just within the region but nationally. One of the early developments was the introduction of the Transport Emergency (TREM) system. This gave advice to emergency service responders on chemical incidents with regard to the nature of the chemical being carried and how it should be dealt with. But this was only the first step in a far more significant attempt to address chemical incidents, which were growing significantly as more and more loads were transferred from railway to road haulage.

In May Mr Dewen, attended a national symposium to discuss a new system called HAZCHEM that was due to be introduced. This new system gave not only information on the properties of the individual chemical and advice on how to contain it, but also advice on how to treat casualties who had been affected by contamination with the chemical. This same system is still in use today by all of the emergency services.

The number of patients carried in 1974 for Durham Health Authority including Darlington was 20,049 emergency and urgent patients and 203,983 outpatients over a total distance of 1,449,927 miles using a total of 151 ambulances.

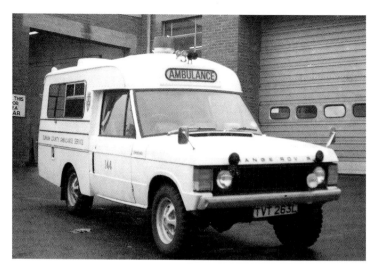

There is no record of the cost of providing this service but it is estimated that it would have been in the region of £900,000. By 1975 the demand for ambulance services within the County had risen dramatically, despite industrial action having reduced the number. In total 26,193 emergency patients and 772 urgent patients were carried, whilst outpatients numbered 241,271. All of these cases involved travelling a total of 1,824,139 miles.

The range of duties (and therefore the level of care provided) continued to expand, for example in 1976 suggestions were made that geriatric patients could be required to attend day units. It was recognised that the transport of these patients would have a major impact on ambulance services, as they were scheduled to arrive at the centres between 9.30 and 10.15am, stay all day and then be home again before dark. This clearly conflicted with the already busy schedule of the service (especially clashing with demands on outpatient transport) and it was felt that extra resources, perhaps dedicated to these units, would be required. An approach was made to social services, to investigate if sharing of resources might be appropriate for these future potential patients and a suggestion of limiting the catchment area of each day unit to 8 miles was made. Little progress on these matters was achieved.

Also during this year it was agreed within the region that each of the local services in the north would (in rotation) provide ambulance transport to and from the Silloth Convalescent Home on the Cumbrian coast. This was a very popular convalescent facility for patients in the region, (predominantly ex-miners), and regular journeys had to be made. In days gone by special trains had been run from County Durham to the home, which had its own small station, but the railway to Silloth closed in 1964. Thereafter it was the duty of the ambulance services, but due to the long journey over the Pennines, the winding road from Carlisle to the coast, and the condition of many of the patients, it was agreed that all journeys would be undertaken only by two man crews.

To cope with the remote territory of upper-Weardale, which boasts the highest 'A' road in the kingdom (the A689 at Killhope Cross), the ambulance station at St. John's Chapel was provided with this modified Range Rover in 1973. It is pictured here at Durham County Council's Central Repair Depot at Framwellgate Moor, which provided all ambulance maintenance at this time.

One surprising comment from 1976 was that the cost of providing a voice recording machine within the control centre was felt to be too great and was therefore not implemented as it was not considered to be essential. Such a machine is absolutely essential to operations today as it records all telephone and radio calls within the control room environment. Patient numbers again rose to 28,599 emergencies, 920 urgent cases and 285,585 outpatients covering 1,698,848 miles.

Although all of the ambulance stations within the county had been built within the last 20 years, with the exception of Darlington (which had previously been the town's Fire Station), many of the stations reflected a measure of post-war austerity. Early in 1977 the Health Authority's Strategic Plan reported that a survey was being undertaken to assess what would be needed to bring them up to present day standards. Some upgrading work had already been commenced at Crook and it was intended that a modest programme of improvements could be sustained elsewhere. The opportunity was also being taken to assess the extent of structural alterations that would be necessary for the service to comply with the requirements of the Sex Discrimination Act. This plan was to be implemented from 1977 through to 1986.

At around the same time discussion took place regarding a suggestion from the Department of Health that the current 999 service number should be discontinued and that each emergency service be issued with its own contact telephone number. It was felt locally that the suggestion was associated with possible economies within the GPO who were responsible for telephone systems at that time. Durham made a recommendation to retain the present 999 service as they considered that it was second to none and that lives would be at risk if it were discontinued or changed. Obviously this view was repeated on a national basis and the 999 system exists to this day virtually unchanged since its inception. It is difficult to comprehend the chaos that would result if there were no central, national number for summoning emergency assistance.

The quality of the service delivered to patients was becoming a more widespread topic. Standards of response for ambulance vehicles to emergency calls had been devised by the Operational Research Consultancy and were widely known as the ORCON Standards. These standards (only advisory and not mandatory in 1977) were that:

i) an ambulance should be despatched within 3 minutes of the control centre receiving the emergency call and;

ii) 50% of ambulances despatched should reach their destination within 8 minutes or less,

iii) 95% should reach their destination in 20 minutes or less.

Because of the difficulty in establishing exactly when an ambulance started its journey to a patient and when it actually arrived, Durham did not begin calculating ORCON during this year. It would, of course, become a mandatory standard in the future, and it is the foundation on which all ambulance services are now judged. Quality of service was also an issue with regard to outpatient as well as emergency patients. The Regional Health Authority decided to implement a pilot site for computerised planning and scheduling of patients who were attending pre-arranged hospital appointments by ambulance. This would be the first such system to be implemented in the whole of the country.

Durham was chosen as an ideal service in terms of population numbers, density and location and a system was installed during 1977. Mike Bell, later to become an Executive Director of the service, was seconded from the regional office to oversee the production of the various mileage and demand matrices that would be necessary to make the system effective. The project was initially intended to have a four-year development period, but Mike ended up being seconded to Durham for 3 years until 1980. During this time he attended many seminars and presentations all over Britain, describing to ambulance and health authorities the features and benefits of this ground-breaking system. The lessons learned in Durham were used to implement other computerised scheduling systems throughout the U.K.

Below:
Another view at the Central Repair Depot, this time in 1976, when a number of Leyland EA ambulances (in both emergency and outpatient specification) with Wadham bodies are seen with a 25cwt Bedford CF emergency ambulance. The Bedford with the Hanlon body was actually owned by Northumbria Ambulance Service, but maintained under contract by Durham County Council's CRD. Courtesy Ron Henderson

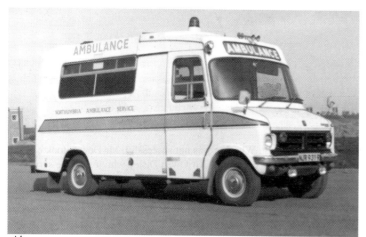

Above:

The vehicles bought in the mid-1970s (the Bedford CF chassis, with a Hanlon body) were of smaller size than the traditional ambulances, which were no longer available. In effect this had removed 40 seats from the overall fleet capacity in Durham because of the lower number of seats in the Bedford CF's. The service estimated that it would need five additional ambulances to make up this shortfall at a cost of £7,000 each. The example seen above was allocated to the Northumbria service, but it was from a batch of vehicles that were allocated to services in the Northern Region, including Durham. Courtesy: Ron Henderson

In 1977 a total of 28,827 emergency patients, 585 urgent patients and 290,382 outpatients were carried. A total of 272 operational staff used 111 vehicles to provide this service, and 44 other staff were employed in support services and management positions. The costs of the service had risen to £1,601,499 in 1977, which was well over half a million pounds more than in 1974. There is evidence that the actual cost of ambulance provision was spiralling, and this was due to both the phenomenal increases in demand and of the considerable external inflationary pressure present during this period.

Consequently the Health Authority Operational Plan for 1978 stated that any significant improvement in services must be discounted in the financial situation then being encountered. It went on to say that any degree of priority for ambulance services would be illogical given the then Government Policy of emphasis on community care over hospital care although other areas of strategy, such as the extension of Day Hospital facilities would need to be examined. It was also acknowledged that the use of the computer based system to plan resource use had reached its capacity and could not be expected to do anything more than ensure that available resources were deployed to the best advantage.

It was therefore agreed that the way to improve ambulance services could only be achieved by reducing demand. Guidelines were prepared to give to hospitals and GPs with a view to encouraging more judicious use of ambulance vehicles.

It was recognised that this was not just a local problem however, but a national trend and that similar action in the past had achieved no long-term effect in curtailing demand. A factor that impacted on the ambulance service's ability to respond to these increasing demands, was the design and specification of the new type of vehicles (with a lower passenger capacity) such as the Ford Transit and the Bedford CF that were then being recommended. The Health Authority identified that even if the Regional Health Authority were willing to approve the purchase of extra ambulances, the local Health Authority would still be faced with the staffing costs . Furthermore there was no spare capacity at existing ambulance stations to accommodate additional staff or vehicles. It was decided that as there were limited opportunities for savings elsewhere in the ambulance service, this solution could not be afforded.

Unfortunately, in the following year, 1979, a staff dispute again resulted in a disruption of the services provided to patients. This was more noticeable in the outpatient service where journeys were severely restricted during the first quarter of the year. The reason for the dispute was once again pay and conditions of service and was resolved in April

In 1979 the Health Authority published its Strategic Plan for the next ten years and it is interesting to note some comments from this plan:-

'The basic problems identified in previous planning documents remain unresolved. Predictably, in the absence of any re-appraisal of the statutory obligations to provide ambulance transport, delegated to Health Authorities, the imbalance between demand and available resources persists and seems likely to continue. Local guidelines on the use of the service, approved by the authority, have been circulated but there is yet no evidence of any marked reduction in workload. As more of the older vehicles in use become due for replacement, the carrying capacity of the fleet is being eroded by the substitution of the smaller standard model and overall mileage increased because of the need to make extra journeys to offset that loss. A compensating increase in vehicle establishment is the logical answer but, assuming this could be funded (at £9,000 per ambulance), there is no unused garage accommodation available.'

It is interesting to note that by now the vehicles' cost had risen to £9,000 each compared with the £7,000 that had been quoted in 1978. This is an indication of the severe level of inflation that was evident in the country at that time.

Right:

During 1979 a report was produced from the Royal Commission on Ambulance Services. This included recommendations that ambulance services might best be delivered if services were tiered, meaning that the emergency and urgent service would be split from the outpatient service, with dedicated staff using dedicated vehicles for each service. It was envisaged by the report that an experimental option might be to have outpatient service provided locally linked to individual hospitals while emergency services could be provided on a regional basis. Here Jan Bradley and Kath McGill lift an elderly patient out of a Bedford CF 'outpatient' ambulance at Highfield Hospital Day Unit.

Up until the Royal Commission Report, all operational staff within Durham were trained to the same level and worked some days on the emergency service and other days transporting outpatients depending on their individual rota. This arrangement continued in the short term but would subsequently change when the ambulance service finally underwent re-organisation in 1986. The number of patients carried in 1979 was 30,460 emergency and urgent patients with 191,059 outpatients. (This number was significantly reduced by the dispute early in the year). Even so, more than 1,600, 000 miles were travelled. The budget had increased by this time to £2,222,663.

Demands on the ambulance service within the County continued to be an issue that the Health Authority wished to pursue. Therefore in 1980 the Authority issued guidance to all hospital departments and GPs on those cases it considered should receive ambulance transport. Although the document was lengthy it did give details of those patients who should specifically **not** receive ambulance transport:-

      Drunken patients from casualty departments;
      Walking patients from casualty departments even after midnight;
      Patients suffering financial difficulties;
      Non-essential escorts.

The budget for the service amounted to £2,937,475 in 1980 and this rose to £3,264,389 in the following year. The next major change to affect the service was yet another re-organisation, this time involving all of the health units funded by the Health Authority. This re-organisation, in 1985, meant that in the future a general manager would head each separate unit. For the County Durham Ambulance Service that resulted in the post of Chief Ambulance Officer becoming redundant and being replaced by the post of Unit General Manager. Consequently, the existing CAO, Mr Dewen, was required to apply under open and external competition for this newly titled post. When he was not successful, Mr Dewen took early retirement. His replacement was Mr Owen Disley who joined the service from Northumbria Ambulance Service in October of that year.

In the years leading up to this change a number of reports had been produced both nationally and locally on the future provision of ambulance services. The Royal Commission Report has already been mentioned and, in addition to this, in 1983 the Health Authority had commissioned the Health Operational Research Unit (HORU) to produce a report specific to County Durham. This latter report was published in July 1984, and it contained some quite radical recommendations on the future of the service.

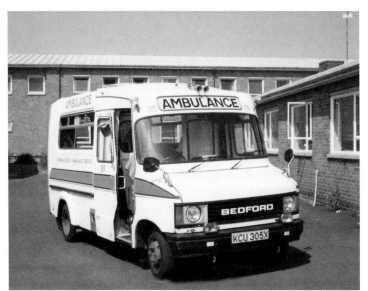

Above:
A 35cwt Bedford CF with twin rear wheels (to outpatient specification) is seen at Bishop Auckland Ambulance Station. Note that whilst it is fitted with two-tone horns, it carries no blue lights.

The new report proposed (amongst other measures) the closure of the stations at Middleton-in-Teesdale, Chester-le-Street, Crook and Fishburn. To offset this it was proposed to increase manning at some other stations, notably, Darlington, Durham and Bishop Auckland. It was a very detailed report, having covered a wide area of research into demand characteristics throughout the County. The recommendations and conclusions were never implemented in the form presented in the report, although some of the recommendations made to the Health Authority in 1988 undoubtedly had their origins within the research carried out by HORU.

Looking back at the arrival of Mr Disley as the new UGM, most observers would point to the tremendous changes that took place. In fact, what is the most remarkable thing is not the amount of change in itself but the speeds at which that change happened. This was in stark contrast with the slow methodical development in the service prior to 1985 which, whilst being innovative to some extent, had been a fairly constrained process. Suddenly in 1986 a very radical and far-reaching review of service was undertaken and implemented. This involved every area of the service from the senior management structure down to the most junior of operational staff. It is a most difficult process to identify which of the changes had the most impact. As to the staff involved, the change that affected them personally will naturally be judged the most important.

With this in mind I will cover in the following paragraphs some of the major changes implemented during 1986 in order of neither priority nor of implementation.

In line with the recommendations made in the Royal Commission Report of 1979 the service was finally tiered and the staff and vehicles were structured to meet either emergency/urgent duties or outpatient transport and routine demands. Up until this time all staff had been qualified in accident and emergency duties but spent most of their time carrying outpatients on routine journeys. This was clearly not making best and most efficient use of their training and skills, so crews were given a choice of opting for either emergency or outpatient work. The levels of pay were to be different and, as far as was possible, staff were allocated to the tier of their choice. Inevitably, however, some people did not end up working on the tier they wished. Linked to this change was the provision of dedicated vehicles, which will be dealt with in a later chapter.

Also to undergo a radical change was the structure of the management. Until 1986 every station had a permanent station officer who was not operational, but took responsibility for running his station and the staff therein. These revisions saw virtually all of the existing station officers either transferred to other duties or encouraged to take early retirement. Only six station officers would be appointed to the following divisions:

Darlington and the outstations in Teesdale;
Bishop Auckland, Crook and Weardale;
Durham and Chester-le-Street;
Newton Aycliffe and Fishburn;
Consett and Stanley;
Peterlee and Seaham.

This basic structure was much modified in coming years with Station Officers becoming fewer and fewer. Those who remained assumed responsibility for additional stations and their duties increased to include liaison with the hospitals and GP practices within their area. They also took responsibility for the investigation of complaints involving their staff or their geographical area of the county, as part of the service's new Complaints' Procedure. In addition several other important changes were made. Maintenance was brought under the direct control of the service with the appointment of a Fleet Engineer. The Service's own workshops were set up next to the headquarters at Framwellgate Moor and from this point onwards, they expanded to undertake the full range of maintenance duties necessary to effectively service the fleet of ambulances and the associated vehicles today. A support services department was also established with Mike Bell, the same person who had undertaken work with the computer system in 1977, being employed by the service as an Assistant Divisional Officer in charge of Support Services. This was unusual in ambulance services as Mike was appointed into a uniformed post although he did not originate from a uniformed background.

Developments were also undertaken to the control system, which (although operating a single control centre for the whole county) had achieved this by operating four smaller controls within the same room. Prior to 1986 each mini-control was responsible for a geographical sector of the county, but the re-organisation amalgamated these four mini-controls into one centralised system. This allowed more flexible and effective deployment of the available resources and resulted in the development of stand-by points for crews. This was a very unpopular concept with the operational staff as it involved them 'standing by' in lay-bys or car parks providing cover for neighbouring stations who were busy.

Under the new management structure there was no longer permanent and guaranteed supervision on stations, and this made the allocation and documentation of fuel supplies to vehicles very difficult to maintain. Giving all staff unrestricted access to petrol supplies was clearly needed to maintain uninterrupted services but the difficulties surrounding safety and documentation were considerable. A study was undertaken and it was decided to install computerised terminals at petrol sites throughout the county. By using two keys (one issued to the individual vehicle and the other a personal issue to the driver) it would be possible to account for fuel issues as the computer read the characteristics of the two keys before switching on the petrol pump. The first such machines were installed in Durham and Darlington but were extended throughout the county in later years.

Following the major changes that took place immediately after Mr Disley's arrival, the following months were taken up with reviewing the demand patterns for the service. As mentioned previously the HORU report had considered this same area. Mr Disley put proposals to the Health Authority in February 1988, regarding the savings that could be made if the number of stations within the county could be reduced. The preferred option of the Health Authority at that time was to restrict the hours worked at a number of stations and it was decided that the stations at Seaham, Stanley, Chester-le-Street and Newton Aycliffe would close between midnight and 8.00 am.

These proposals were never actually implemented, as there was a public and staff outcry at the reduction of services this would entail. Any closure of an ambulance station is always a difficult decision and is guaranteed to extract an emotive response from both the media and public and this was certainly the case in this instance! But even so, there is no doubt that overall efficiency was improving. It will be recalled that the standard of response at that time was that ambulances should arrive at 95% of all emergency calls within 20 minutes but in 1988 the service actually achieved 99%!

Owen Disley stayed with the service only a relatively short time before taking up a Chief Ambulance Officer's post with Mersey Metropolitan Ambulance Service in June 1988. Immediately following his departure David Todhunter acted as UGM until Mr Ken Threlfall took up the post on 11th July 1988. As a matter of interest David Todhunter actually followed Mr Disley to Merseyside, first as his deputy and ultimately as his successor. Shortly after the arrival of Mr Threlfall the new Motorola radio system (which had been commissioned before his appointment) was installed in the control room. This system allowed full data transmission and revolutionised the operation within control. Speech transmission was now kept to a minimum as all aspects of routine work could be given a numerical code and control could be kept informed of a crew's exact detailed status without the need to talk.

A Trio of Senior Officers,
Top: *The last Chief Ambulance Officer George Dewen (right) is seen at Bishop Auckland Station presenting a gift to Joe Broadbent on his retirement as station manager in 1982.*

Centre: *Seen at a presentation of certificates to a new group of paramedics in 1989, the new UGM Owen Disley is seen to the right of the picture in the dark suit. The officer on the left is ADO Mike Leonard (communications), the author of this book.*

Right: *Ken Threlfall, Unit General Manager/Chief Executive 1993.*

Left

The first paramedics were introduced into the service in 1987 (see training section), but only in very limited numbers. As it would be some time before the number of qualified staff increased substantially, it was therefore decided that a system of deployment needed to be developed. To this end a rapid response scheme was set up with the paramedics being deployed in cars to any emergency call that control considered might need paramedic intervention. In addition, other crews could call out a paramedic if they considered it was in a patient's interest to do so. The cars that the paramedics used (like this Maestro at Bishop Auckland) were fitted with blue beacons and two-tone horns as well as a range of appropriate equipment. This scheme continued for a number of years until the number of paramedics in the service had increased to such an extent that there were sufficient to allow the majority of ambulance crews to be made up of one paramedic and one ambulance technician. Once this was the case then the separate deployment of paramedics in cars became an unnecessary duplication of response and the scheme was discontinued.

The allocation of shifts and operation of station rotas were becoming increasingly difficult to administer, especially now that a number of differing grades of staff were being used, and to assist in this process a new department was established. Known as the Manpower Planning Department, it was started by Station Officer John Hayes and Leading Ambulanceman Peter Stoddart. Commencing from Consett station on 16th September 1988, it took only 6 weeks to centralise the whole system. Complete cover for the county shift system was produced by the MPU by 1st November 1988. It was initially worked on paper, but the next logical step was to computerise and develop the system. In 1999, this department is now central to the whole of the organisation, for today it not only allocates shifts, holidays and lieu days but collates sickness and absence records and is a prime tool in departmental budgetary control.

Management changes were also made during this period, and in 1989 mobile supervisors were appointed (initially on secondment). The theory was that these supervisors would replace the Leading Ambulancemen at the stations, and cover their area by using a car or other light service vehicle. These supervisors would be mobile around the county on a 24-hour basis, and there was one on duty for the north of the county and one for the south. They travelled round the stations doing the administrative work of each station during the visit, replenishing stores and dealing with staff queries as appropriate. Eventually these posts were made substantive in 1990 following interviews. At about this time the service was divided into two operational divisions North and South with each division being run by an Assistant Divisional Officer (ADO) who both reported to the Divisional Officer Operations. Each ADO had a Sub-Divisional Manager who supervised the Mobile Supervisors within his division.

In April 1991 the ORCON standard changed in that ambulances were now required to reach 95% of all emergency calls within 19 minutes, a minute quicker than previously. In this first year of the new standard Durham achieved a 95.9% response and this was bettered in 1992/93 when the service reached 97.1% of calls within the 19-minute target time. Demand had increased to more than 30,000 emergency calls this year with 15,000 urgent cases.

A major change in management arrangements came in 1992 with the opportunity for ambulance services to apply for Trust status. This meant that as a Trust the service became financially independent with many more freedoms as to how it conducted its finances. Leading up to the application for Trust status the service appointed a Business Development Manager in 1991 followed by a Quality Assurance Manager in 1992 who developed the application to become a Trust from 1st April 1993. Today almost every ambulance service in the UK is a trust and it has become the expected and conventional model of modern health service management.

Thereafter, the ambulance service would be administered by a Trust Board, which would be headed by a Chairman, Mrs Pat Wynne OBE (later to become CBE) assisted by five Non-Executive members of the board all appointed by the Secretary of State for Health. The executive members of the board would be the Chief Executive (formerly the UGM) assisted by four executive directors covering the areas of Operations, Human Resources, Finance and Fleet. The only person not already employed was the Director of Finance who had to be appointed to administer the new financial freedoms the Trust now enjoyed. One of these freedoms enjoyed as a Trust was the authority to run the ambulance service on more business-like lines.

This meant that the service now had the opportunity to raise its budget by earning additional income from business ventures. Very early in the life of the new Trust it was decided that 'Income Generation' would only be contemplated if it had a direct link into health provision and involved using skills that were already used within the Trust. This was demonstrated by the slogan used at the time of 'We invest in the NHS'.

With these parameters in mind the Business Manager, John Hehir, along with appropriate operational managers and colleagues negotiated a number of income generation schemes to provide added value to the health care of County Durham which would, in addition, supplement the contract income of the Trust. This additional income would be used to offset the year on year real term savings that the Trust was required to make under the modern financial arrangements that were now being used.

In addition to the above the fleet workshops were then to be run as a commercial enterprise. Whilst the repair of ambulance vehicles would always take priority they were empowered to develop commercial awareness and to maximise the use of their resources by building up a customer base outside of the service. Over the years this has proved to be very effective with the staff in the fleet maintenance section gaining accreditation to carry out MOT tests on the full range of vehicles as well as being accredited by Renault and Ford as service agents. Many other income generation schemes would also be run and the principle has become an accepted part of running a modern ambulance service. The operation of these schemes has, however, always been a secondary function of the core business which is entirely patient focused.

Below:
The Chairman of the new NHS Trust, Mrs. Pat Wynne (right) is pictured presenting Ailsa Rutter with an Instructors Certificate in Criteria Based Despatch (CBD). The bonus of the CBD system was that it also allowed control staff to give informed advice to the caller so that they could assist the patient before the ambulance arrival.

Above:
One of the new income generation schemes included a Doctors' Co-operative in North Durham, which started in June of 1994. This involved the ambulance control providing call centre facilities for a group of GP practices on an out-of-hours basis. Calls were then passed to a visiting car service using GPs from the co-operative members who were driven to the calls by ambulance staff in cars especially procured for the scheme. The cars used for this scheme were Ford Escort Turbo Diesel saloons.

In January 1994, shortly after the change to Trust status, Ken Threlfall moved to South Yorkshire Metropolitan Ambulance Service as its new Chief Executive. Following this, David Marshall (Director of Operations) was appointed acting-Chief Executive until Robert Alabaster took up the post in March. Interestingly, Mr. Alabaster would be the first head of the Durham service that did not have an ambulance service background. After his appointment, a review of the current management structure was undertaken and as a result the Board was reduced in size. This saw the abolition of the post of one executive director (fleet) and one non-executive director. The management of fleet would remain a major part of the service despite these changes, but thereafter it was the operational service director who would represent these interests at board level.

Over the next five years a programme of new and previously unheard of management issues would be explored and developed to reflect the changes in the NHS. Amongst the new changes was a further review of management and its structure in 1996, which resulted in the Directorate of Human Resources being replaced with a personnel department (not board level). Significantly, the Operations Directorate was split into two parts, thus providing a Director of Accident and Emergency Services and Director of Non Emergency Services. This split was promoted to ensure that each side of the operational service had an equal opportunity at board level to promote their differing needs and requirements.

Above:
Robert Alabaster (centre) joined the Trust having previously been the Assistant General Manager at the Royal Infirmary, Edinburgh. The experience gained by Mr Alabaster in the wider health service undoubtedly helped to lead the new programme of change and improvement, which reflected the need for ambulance services to be an integral and effective part of a modern health service.

When resources are short in ambulance services, historically it is always tempting to allocate those resources to the high profile life-saving emergency service. Of course the needs of patients in the non-emergency service are always important, but from this change onwards to the present day they had the Non-Emergency Directorate championing their needs at board level. This extended in 1998 to each directorate having their own management structure with the appointment of PTS locality managers, who undertook responsibility for individual contracts within their remit.

Communication had become an increasingly important issue, for with the accelerating pace of change within the health service as a whole (and the ambulance service in particular), it was becoming essential to develop strong communication lines to ensure that staff and managers were aware of current issues. The *Staff Information Bulletin* (a station and departmental notice issued weekly) started by Owen Disley in 1986, whilst still useful, was no longer proving to be adequate in reacting to the pace of change being experienced.

To resolve the communications problem a regular series of 'Chief Executive Briefing Sessions' was established in 1996. Managers would, from this date, be given a group briefing following each monthly board meeting. The information given would then be cascaded to staff on stations and departments. Additional, short notice briefings could be arranged if necessary. Another change that took place was the introduction of a clinical audit department in 1997 to oversee the clinical effectiveness of staff and the procedures used. This would extend into a much higher profile for clinical and corporate governance by 1998.

Also in 1997 the Board introduced measures by which the overall performance of the Trust could be judged. Known as Key Performance Indicators (KPIs), they identified what the overall performance was each month and provided information to the Board that showed the actual performance in relation to the agreed targets. The nature of the service provided by control continued to change over this period. In 1996 a computerised command and control system was installed, which revolutionised the method of despatch for emergency vehicles and provided the service with very clear statistical data on a wide variety of operational matters. This system was complemented by the installation of a prioritisation system for 999 calls, which was installed in late1998.

This latter system of Criteria Based Despatch allows the call-taker to prioritise the incoming 999 call into either category A, B or C. Category A is life threatening, Category B is serious but not life threatening and Category C is minor. The system, using computer based algorithms, allows the information from the caller to be assessed, gives prompts to ensure that as much information as is possible is gathered and then advises on the prioritisation the call should receive. The installation of this system was vital if the service was to be able to achieve new national performance targets by the deadline of 2001. These new targets are that 75% of Category A calls should be arrived at within eight minutes of the call being placed. All other calls would receive the existing standard of arrival within 19 minutes. By 1996/97 the service achieved 95.2% of its calls within the 19 minute standard but had seen demand rise to more than 35,200 emergency calls and 16,000 urgent calls. To cope with this demand the service budget had risen to £9,039,000 in 1997/98.

Below:
One of the new income generation schemes was the Clinical Waste Collection Service, which was developed to collect this type of waste and transport it to authorised incineration plants. In this view Brian Warriner is seen loading one of the Mercedes Sprinter vans used on this service. Note that it carries the Durham County Ambulance lettering on the side.

Staff and Estates

The change from Local Authority to Health Service control in April 1974 was not a clear-cut break in responsibility and reporting lines for staff. Although management and reporting responsibility changed to a Health Service base through Health Authorities, the geographical boundaries did not change immediately. This meant that some of the stations affected by those changes, namely Winlaton, Hebburn, Washington and New Herrington which were due to be transferred to the new Tyne & Wear Metropolitan Ambulance Service, remained as part of Durham County Ambulance Service for some months until a formal transfer date was arranged. Staff were formally notified on 24th April 1974 that the title of the new ambulance service within the new County of Durham was to be Durham County Ambulance Service. As a consequence of these changes, the staffing level within County Durham during 1974 was 19 Depot Superintendents, 315 ambulancemen, 16 trainees, three vehicle maintenance staff, six admin. and clerical, 19 control staff and two officers, although these numbers would reduce as the above depots transferred to their new authority. Staff who had transferred into the NHS carried with them their existing terms and conditions of employment.

Only a short time later, however, in early 1975 there was considerable disruption to service as staff took industrial action in pursuit of improved wages and terms of service. As a result of this, agreements were finalised for the accommodation of all staff in operational employment with the ambulance service to be paid under Whitley Council national rates of pay. This included ambulancemen and ambulance officers. There were no women employed on operational duties at this time and a further ten years would elapse before this situation changed. Following the agreement made and, in conjunction with national guidelines on rank structure within ambulance services, Durham County Ambulance Service decided to reclassify all of their Depot Superintendents as Rank 6 Station Officers and all Senior Ambulancemen would now be called Leading Ambulancemen.

The status and recognition of ambulance staff was further developed as discussions began in 1977 regarding the issue of a long service award to ambulance staff. These discussions revolved around length of service required, whether only uniformed staff qualified and what previous occupations could be classed as service.

Some staffing difficulties arose again in 1979 when the Health Authority Strategic Plan revealed that some increase in staffing might be required, as staff in the 'out-stations' were expressing an unwillingness to continue supplying 'stand-by' cover. The only alternative would be to provide 24-hour cover for these areas from existing or new stations. However, it is clear that a resolution was found for this concern, as 20 years later stand-by cover is still found to be the most effective cover arrangement for the sparsely populated areas of the County. This method of cover has continued on an uninterrupted basis in Teesdale and, although such arrangements proved to be unsustainable in Weardale they have recently been re-introduced as we will cover at a later stage.

Above:
The Leyland EA ambulance seen at Washington was one of the vehicles that transferred out of the Durham County service along with the depot following the local government reorganisation in 1974. The staff at those transferred depots although theoretically part of Tyne & Wear continued to be paid and managed by Co. Durham. Courtesy: Ron Henderson

Below:
This specially-equipped 4-wheel drive Ford Transit was obtained by the service as its Special Incident Vehicle for use at major incidents. It carried an 'Airshell' shelter which could house 19 stretcher casualties and its own independent heating and lighting systems.

Above:

As part of the Station upgrade review that was taking place in 1979, it was identified that Darlington Station, despite having been improved as much as was possible, still remained unsatisfactory. It concluded that new accommodation should be sought as a mid-term objective of the capital programme of the ten-year plan. Darlington eventually moved into new accommodation for the emergency service at the Memorial Hospital in 1990 some 11 years behind schedule with outpatient staff (later called PTS or Patient Transport Service) not moving until 14th November 1997 to a new station at Morton Park on the edge of the town. The picture above shows the official opening of the new PTS premises by The Rt. Hon. Alan Milburn, Minister of State for Health with Mrs. Pat Wynne CBE.

Industrial action by ambulance crews was evident again on 27th June 1982 when staff held a one-day protest in pursuit of a pay claim and, as all cover was withdrawn, the police were asked to assist with the handling of emergency calls. This action, part of national negotiations, was repeated again in September, when a limited emergency service was provided. This year also saw a number of other grades within the Health Service in County Durham resorting to industrial action; including storekeepers, pharmacists, accounts personnel and administration staff.

March 1985 saw the appointment of a new member of staff, and this would forever change the face of Durham County Ambulance Service, as this was the first female operational member of staff to be employed by the service. Up until this time all the ambulance crews had been male, but Bernadette Williamson would be the forerunner of many women in the service, finally dispelling the myth that it was 'a mans job'. As described earlier a major change to staff was the introduction of a tiered service in 1986, with qualifications appropriate to the work they undertook and payment rates that reflected this.

Along with this was a major change in the way ambulance crews were paid, as a salaried structure for staff was introduced with monthly pay instead of weekly. New rates were agreed nationally through the Whitley Council. Shortly after this the first paramedics were trained and additional payments of £650 per year were made to reflect their additional skills. Also in 1986, a new category of staff was employed and for the first time part-time staff were employed on operational duties within the service. They were employed for 30 hours per week and mainly carried patients into and out of day units. The employment of part-timers extended in 1989 to 15 hour working. This is the model that continues to this day with staff working a three-shift system from 8am to 11am, 11.30am to 2.30pm and from 3pm to 6pm. Many of the people who were employed under these early part-time schemes are still with the service, some having progressed through the tiers of the service to become paramedics.

Left:

By 1989 the service was experiencing difficulty in maintaining adequate cover in Weardale due to the difficulties in recruiting staff, because those staff who worked at St Johns Chapel were required to work 'stand-by' which meant that they must live only a short distance from the station. This severely limited the potential employees and it resulted in stand-by cover being discontinued and additional staff being recruited in the Crook area who would travel into the Dale as and when required. Because of the difficulty in providing an adequate service, for the upper dale in particular, a full stand-by service was re-instated in 1998 following a comprehensive recruitment drive both locally and nationally. Seen outside the station are the two vehicles based there; on the left a 1991 Land Rover Defender with a Rover Special Operations body, complete with winch, which can tackle the most severe winter conditions. On the right a 1996 Mercedes Diesel Sprinter with a UVG Premia body which allows two stretcher patients to be carried side by side. Mechanically it has twin rear wheels with limited slip differential for the worst winter road conditions.

An innovative scheme to improve the standard of care given to patients in Teesdale was started in January 1990, which involved training all staff who worked at these stations in defibrillation and cardiac monitoring. The machines used were purchased by a fund raising effort within Teesdale and by public subscription. The local community took the advance in care very seriously and it was a reflection of the additional support patients in the Teesdale area might need due to the long distances to be travelled to the nearest hospital (Darlington). The staff would be called Cardiac Care Technicians and this standard of care has since been extended to all members of operational staff who are not paramedics. At about the same time as this occurred, emergency staff from Darlington station were at long last provided with newer if much smaller accommodation. They moved into a crew room at Darlington Memorial Hospital near the Accident & Emergency department. This afforded the added benefit of reinforcing liaison links with casualty staff. It would, however, be 1997 before the Darlington PTS staff were moved to new premises.

The saddest event to occur in recent years was the loss of a colleague who was killed whilst on duty. On 10th May 1993 Les Meighan was attending a patient in the rear of his ambulance after his driver Bob Walton had stopped to assist at a road accident on the A19.

Despite the fact that the ambulance was pulled to the side of the road and was showing both hazard warning flashers and its emergency blue beacons, a heavy goods vehicle travelling in the same direction as the ambulance ran into the back of it. The patient escaped relatively unscathed and was transferred to another ambulance for onward transport to hospital, but Les was killed and Bob never returned to work and subsequently retired through ill health. This is the only recorded death of a member of the Durham County Ambulance Service whilst on active duty, but Les Meighan will never be forgotten by his colleagues, for on completion of the ambulance training centre in Durham the following year, the library/study area was dedicated to his memory.

Following the arrival of Robert Alabaster in 1994 there was much discussion about the image and protection of ambulance staff. It was an unpleasant fact that staff members felt themselves to be in danger whilst carrying out their duties, especially at night, on the Accident & Emergency service. The possibility that a member of staff should face the threat of, or actually be a victim of, assault was completely unacceptable.

A factor in this threat was felt to be the similarity between the ambulance service uniform and the police uniform, for the crew's apparel certainly had an authoritarian look. The hunt was on for an alternative and the criteria was that it should be practical in use, easily washed and maintained and that it should project an image that would clearly identify the wearer as a member of the ambulance service. Throughout 1995 evaluations of possible uniforms took place and the final choice of style was put to a staff ballot. With a majority of 84% to 26% the choice was to opt for the squad suit overall which came in two weights (for winter and summer wear) and was green in colour. The maintenance was very easy as they were drip dry and non-iron. They proved to be very popular and practical in use after they were introduced in April 1996.

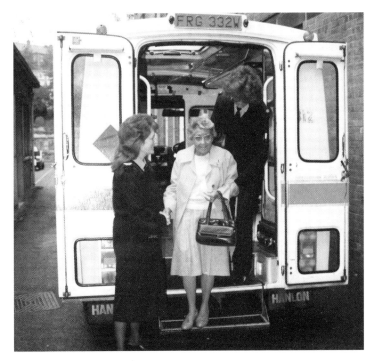

Above:
The first female member of operational staff Bernadette Williamson (right) with colleague Sandra Raine at Shotley Bridge Hospital. .
Below:
The dedication and skill of staff was given Royal approval in 1996 when the Queen agreed that long service medals for Accident and Emergency staff could be issued by the Crown. The first ceremony was held in September 1996 when the Lord Lieutenant David Grant presented 41 members of staff with their medals.

Fleet and Vehicle Equipment

Following the 1974 re-organisation there was little change in the fleet procurement procedure nor the specification and type of vehicles ordered. The majority of development over the medium term would be in respect of vehicle safety and in December 1975 it was decided that all ambulance vehicles should be fitted with hazard warning flasher units. The County Council Central Repair Depot began a programme of fitting these to the vehicles as they were seen for routine maintenance or repair.

Economies were also to be found in the bulk purchase of ambulances, and with this in mind the Chief Ambulance Officers within the northern region made joint decisions regarding the future provision and design of ambulances. As a result all new vehicles were to be based on the Bedford CF chassis with custom bodies supplied by the Irish makers Hanlon. Standard vehicles would have a bulkhead between the driver and saloon but sitting case vehicles would have only a modesty screen. Individual authorities would have the choice of either dark or clear windows for the saloon, but it was unanimously agreed that saloon heaters would be desirable. Equipment levels and specifications of vehicles continued to rise with front repeaters for the blue emergency beacons being seen for the first time and an increase in specification to include rear fog lights.

Additionally, ambulances were now to be fitted with power points for incubators to allow the transfer of small babies to be conducted safely over longer distances. Interestingly the service was, for the first time, to face the problem of carrying patient aids such as wheelchairs and mobility equipment. It was clear that staff felt a reluctance to carry these items of equipment as there was nowhere to store them safely, and their managers agreed that under Health and Safety guidelines provision should be made.

In response the national working group on vehicle design and specification was asked to consider safe storage or fastenings for such equipment to either the ambulance wall or floor. All ambulance vehicles supplied were now specified to contain essential equipment on delivery. This included the Laerdal Suction Unit, Entonox equipment (Pain relief gas sometimes called gas and air) and Scoop stretchers (a full length stretcher that splits open at each end to allow an injured person to be picked up with the minimum of distress).

The new vehicles with their fibreglass bodies, were purchased as a single contract and each of the regional ambulance services was allocated vehicles from this central supply. The replacement programme allowed for vehicles to be replaced at 7-year intervals with an expected mileage of 140,000 miles per vehicle during that time, but problems were destined to occur. The most serious difficulty was identified in November 1978 when a wheel fell off one of the 25cwt. Bedford CF ambulances without warning. This matter was reported and it was discovered that the Scottish Ambulance Service had been experiencing difficulty with this same problem on their Bedford 25 cwt. chassis vehicles. This problem was to plague the service over the next three years and there was another incident of a wheel falling off early in 1979. As a result the Department of Health took up the matter with the manufacturers Vauxhall Motors on a national level. Locally, investigations were made to try to establish how this phenomenon happened: so vehicles were run without hubcaps and paint marks were put on the studs and nuts to show when the nuts were loosening. Staff, although concerned with the problem, actually profited from this investigation as ambulances were sent out with simulated loads (sand bags) on long trips in an attempt to identify under what conditions the problem occurred. This meant that crews were brought in on overtime rates of pay, did not have to carry patients and with the service's blessing had days out to the coast etc. to undertake the mileage necessary to test the vehicles.

Left:

After the Miller Report, recommendations were made regarding the future design of ambulances and considerable changes were proposed, resulting in a move from the older, heavier style of chassis and coach-built body that had been the traditional ambulance of the 1950s and '60s. With the development of the chassis-cab concept of light vans, on to which new glass fibre bodies could be fitted, the firms of Ford and Bedford took the lead in the supply of ambulances. Firms like Dennis, Commer/Karrier, Austin/Morris (now British Leyland), and others fought a rearguard action, but most ambulance authorities standardised on either the Ford Transit or Bedford CF. Durham chose the latter, and the initial vehicles were to the type seen left, which had the standard Bedford metal cab. Later vehicles had cabs integral within the glass-fibre body. Ron Henderson

Right:
Durham's problems with the Bedford CF's continued throughout 1980, but little assistance was offered on a national level. Locally it was decided that carrying eight patients was perhaps too heavy a weight for the chassis and that overloading of the vehicles might be contributing to the problem. As a result these vehicles were, for a time, restricted to carrying just five patients further adding to resource problems within the service. The problem had been fully discussed at the Health Authority and it was agreed to replace Durham's 59 vehicles with the new ambulances on the Bedford 35cwt chassis. This came with commercial suspension and wheels, but the downside was that the upgrade to this chassis type cost an additional £30,000. The ill-fated fleet of 25cwt CF's is seen here awaiting disposal at Earls House Hospital just outside Durham.

The problems affecting ambulance wheels continued without resolution through 1981. Despite having renewed all of the hubs and nuts and restricting the load on the affected vehicles the problems continued to occur. After an incident in Crook on 23rd March 1981, when a loose wheel almost hit another vehicle causing an accident, all 42 vehicles affected were taken out of service.

In order to continue to provide an emergency service the ambulance service had to restrict the number of routine patients that it carried and in the first instance patients attending physiotherapy departments were affected. These patients were asked to find alternative ways of attending hospital by taxi, bus or private transport. The Health Authority assisted in this by asking all neighbouring Health authorities and ambulance users to restrict requests for transport to only 'the most needy cases'. While these problems were being tackled, progress in other areas was being made especially with regard to vehicles designed to deal with rough terrain. A 4-wheel drive Hanlon ambulance purchased by the Northumbria Ambulance Service was evaluated and subsequently these ambulances would be used at all out-stations within County Durham.

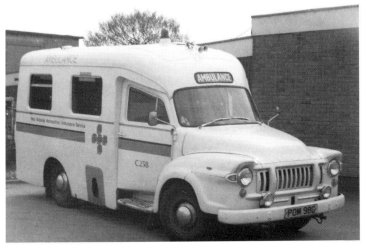

In 1979 fuel restrictions reduced petrol deliveries to the ambulance service by 5% due to difficulties in the Persian Gulf. As ambulance services received no additional allowance in respect of petrol deliveries, Durham decided to take its ambulances off the road for one day per month during which times they would operate an emergency and urgent service only. Alternative fuel sources were also explored with interest being shown in converting ambulances to run on LPG (Liquefied Petroleum Gas). Trials in West Yorkshire Metropolitan Ambulance Service (WYMAS) had shown that savings resulted from reduced fuel costs linked to reduced maintenance and longer engine life. The savings in a single year were said to more than offset the cost of conversion (£264 per vehicle) and WYMAS converted 29 ambulances in their fleet.

Along with other Chief Officers in the Northern Region, it was agreed that one vehicle be converted to monitor any savings and long-term benefits that were made. Cleveland Ambulance Service subsequently converted a considerable number of vehicles, although the other local services did not follow suit. Considerable strain on budgets was also being experienced by all of the services within the region due to the escalating fuel costs incurred by the Gulf Crisis.

Left:
As a result of the CF wheel failures it was agreed not to take out of service some elderly BMC ambulances and to extend their life as long as spares were available. The bodies from the 25cwt ambulances could be transferred onto the 35cwt chassis at considerable cost, but even so additional 35cwt ambulances would have to be bought. As a stopgap, the service arranged to 'borrow' surplus ambulances from a number of other authorities around the country to supplement short-term demands and it would be 1985 before the fleet was back to full strength. One of the loaned vehicles was this 1968 Bedford TJ, which retained its West Midlands Ambulance Service livery whilst working in County Durham.
Both pictures: Courtesy Ron Henderson

Left:

This Bedford coach was purchased by the service for the dual role of Mobile Information Unit and Mobile Command Unit. Although it fortunately never turned a wheel in anger, it was widely used in the consultation process leading up to the adoption of NHS Trust status.

Centre:

When Mr Threlfall arrived in 1988 another review of fleet was undertaken and mindful of the difficulties that had been experienced when the single-make fleet of Bedford's had proved to be a problem a decision was made to develop a multi-manufacturer fleet. Alternative suppliers were sought and both Ford and Mercedes ambulances were purchased in future years. Fourteen Mercedes vehicles were delivered in 1991, but whilst these were purpose designed for either Emergency or PTS use, they were all based on a van conversion rather than a chassis with specialist body. As the skills and equipment used by operational staff increased over the years, the space provided in the rear of van conversion ambulances was to prove to be a limiting factor. In 1992 the situation was re-appraised and the service again reverted to the chassis cab design with Glass Re-inforced Plastic (GRP) bodies for its emergency fleet. These ambulances would be either Ford or Mercedes based and they proved to be a very satisfactory design as the staff had been instrumental in giving advice on the internal layout of these vehicles.

Bottom:

A considerable fleet of Renault vehicles was built up over coming years and while the emergency ambulances maintained the white body colour, they changed the colour of the high visibility stripe to lime/yellow with blue edging. Some of the first Renault PTS vehicles however, went back to being green in colour to distinguish them from the emergency fleet. This trend, however, did not continue and future vehicles after this first allocation returned to white.

Although the fuel supply situation improved by 1980, the procurement policy and type of vehicle used by the service did not and almost every vehicle in the fleet was a Bedford with the Hanlon custom-made body. This continued until the arrival of Mr Disley in 1985 when a re-evaluation of vehicle specifications took place and Renault vehicles were ordered. The first of these arrived in 1986 and were designed to be specific to their role. Emergency vehicles were purpose built, even to the extent of providing hand-washing facilities. Although equipped to far lesser specifications, the PTS vehicles were equally need-oriented and ordered with extremely low load heights to minimise the lifting carried out by staff. Whilst the design of these Renault ambulances meant a very low floor and load height, further improvements were made by the fitting of a tail-lift. On the PTS vehicles this meant that patients did not have to walk up steps or be carried by staff if they were unable to walk. A number of vehicles were fitted with these lifts and they proved to be very successful, being fitted to future ambulances of other makes. The service also purchased a small fleet of Austin Maestro cars at this time, for use as 'service cars' by managers on operational duties.

The continued lifting of patients in and out of emergency ambulances had become unacceptable by 1996, due to the continued incidences of back injury being experienced by staff. The service had explored a number of options over previous years including easy load stretchers but none of them removed completely the need for staff to bear weight at some point of the move into the ambulance. With the increasing popularity and availability of lowering suspension the use of a ramp at the rear of the ambulance became not only feasible but also sensible.

It is ironic that, as can be seen from the small inset photograph (of a Wilson & Stockall bodied ambulance with wheeled trolley stretcher), this was not ground breaking technology. It was merely a return to the methods used some 90 years previously. However, it was very successful and this system is used on all of the recent additions to the fleet since 1996.

Another new innovation is being adopted as this book goes to press, as certain members of staff are currently being trained to provide a Motorcycle Paramedic Scheme. This will become operational during March 1999 and will hopefully be extended into the following financial year to become an integral part of the Trust's emergency responses. The bikes used will be Honda Pan European ST1100 similar to those used by the police and neighbouring services. They will be equipped with defibrillator, pulse oximeter and other paramedic equipment.

Top:
One of the Maestro saloon cars used by the paramedics, this vehicle was sponsored by the local motor engineers Fred Henderson, and given a distinctive livery to reflect this. Pictured is Paramedic Kevin Wadge.

Centre:
The service built up its own workshop facilities and a competent team of mechanics, including (from left to right) John Towers, Doug Barraclough, Alan Smailes, Barry Simpson and Brian Webster, who are pictured with the Vauxhall Astra maintenance van.

Right:
One of the new High Dependency Paramedic units outside Shotley Bridge Hospital. These vehicles are based on the Ford Transit chassis with a UGV Customline Lazer body. They carried 12-lead ECG equipment and a FAX machine linked to a mobile 'phone to send details of the patient's ECG and general condition directly to the hospital ahead of their arrival.

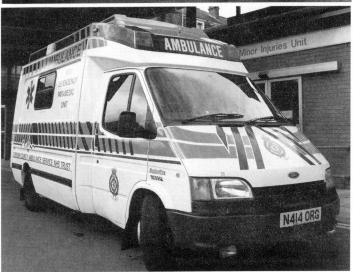

Training and Ambulance Care Equipment

The levels of training that are given to new entrants to the emergency service today, are basically little different to those being given after the reorganisation in 1974. The applicants back then received 2 weeks induction training followed by 6 weeks basic training at the regional ambulance school in Keighley, West Yorkshire. This centre continued for a considerable number of years before it eventually closed, and thereafter each service became responsible for its own training arrangements. The time spent on training today is similar to that received by staff in the '70s, but the content of the course has been much refined. Strangely, and in contrast to the first few years of the NHS service, the one main element of training that was not compulsory was driver training. Indeed during 1974 the Department of Health embarked on a programme of Driving Instructor Training for ambulance services and by August it had appointed 22 trained instructors nationally, but they were still campaigning for many more. The intention was to train all ambulance personnel in driving although this would remain as a voluntary element of training for some years.

As mentioned earlier, following the Miller Report, the equipment levels of ambulances were now being improved. By 1975 the use of Suction Units manufactured by Laerdal (first introduced in 1971) was common, with a unit being placed on every ambulance designated for emergency use. The design of this equipment has changed little over the years, and almost identical equipment is still in use on Durham County ambulances in 1999. This design of suction equipment, which is used to clear a patient's airway of blood, vomit or other obstruction, is still the first choice of Durham staff and an essential tool used in patient care.

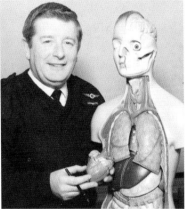

Paramedic George Mooney demonstrates a S&W DMS730 Defribilator and monitor.

For the protection of ambulance crews, local discussions highlighted the desirability of providing protective helmets and the feasibility of this was investigated. Another item of equipment specifically designed for use by ambulance staff was a new Maternity Pack. This pack contained one gown, three green towels, two kidney dishes, one bowl, one gallipot, one pair of scissors and two artery forceps. The provision of this equipment, supplied by the Central Sterile Supplies Department at Dryburn Hospital, was an acknowledgement of the additional training received and professionalism that ambulance staff now displayed. In 1978 a decision was taken that all ambulances within County Durham would carry Sabre Saturn Oxygen resuscitators and therapy units. Previously medium concentration of oxygen had been available to patients, but this new equipment allowed the administration of 100% oxygen to patients who needed resuscitation with the facility to warn the operator if the patient's airway was blocked. This was a considerable step forward in patient care.

The Training School Manager John Burns and an anatomical dummy in 1996.

During a meeting of Chief Ambulance Officers from the Northern Region on 18th September 1979 came the first mention of the single most important improvement to patient care that occurred within ambulance services nationally. That is 'Extended Training' which was the first name applied to Paramedic Training. A DHSS Seminar had been held in Harrogate to discuss the future of ambulance services, and a Report from the Royal Commission on Ambulance Services had been presented at this seminar as well as a paper entitled *Advanced Training for Ambulance Personnel* and this resulted in general agreement that:

i   Before the introduction of advanced training for ambulance personnel, it was essential to ensure that basic and post-proficiency or 'in-service training' requirements were properly satisfied.

ii   Advanced training schemes should be properly established with the support and co-operation of hospital medical and nursing staff.

iii   Advanced training would provide a basis for further tiering of the service.

With the future of staff training in mind, discussions began locally with neighbouring services about the introduction of selection testing for future employees. It was agreed that this was desirable, as ambulance personnel were now having to considerably develop their skills and that recruitment of the required standard of staff could only be guaranteed through careful and consistent testing.

In addition to the above, Durham's Chief Ambulance Officer, George Dewen fully supported staff in the County who applied for permission to join and study for the Ambulance Service Institute qualifications. Although voluntary and not required as a mandatory qualification within ambulance services, such qualifications were highly regarded and he expressed the view that staff who attained these qualifications benefited their individual services.

Paramedic Mike Simpson with a display of modern paramedic ambulance equipment.

It would be 1987 before the first paramedics were introduced into the service in County Durham. These staff trained in Northumbria for four weeks followed by a period of six weeks spent in hospital undergoing specialist practical training under the guidance of hospital consultants. This remains the model for paramedic training today.

The introduction of paramedics brought about a complete review of ambulance equipment and many items were upgraded. These included resuscitation units from Pneupak and later Sabre-Mars, a change from inflatable splints to vacuum splints, the procurement of defibrillators and other specialised paramedic equipment such as blood pressure cuffs, laryngoscopes, forceps etc. Other equipment additions occurred with the introduction across the whole service of pulse oximeters (a non-invasive machine to measure the oxygen saturation of the blood) in 1995 followed closely by the wider introduction of whole body vacuum splints to support casualties suffering multiple trauma.

The new Trust invested in a purpose built, residential training centre, based at Earls House Hospital in Durham and on 15th April 1994 the new centre was opened by HRH the Duchess of Kent. It was to receive accreditation to conduct its own paramedic and basic training courses, and as a result it was to provide a huge expansion in the training conducted by the service. In future years the training centre went on to provide specialist training for ships captains and senior officers from British Petroleum, first aid at work courses for industry, driving courses for commercial customers and training for other ambulance services.

Training extended further into the community in August of 1998 when a paramedic was seconded under a regional initiative called 'Lifelink' to improve the level of resuscitation skills for members of the public. This was a joint initiative with Humberside and North Yorkshire ambulance services and the aim was to train 1,500 members of the public within the year of secondment. Kevin Fitzpatrick, the paramedic seconded to Lifelink in Durham, is well ahead of this target at the time of writing and it is hoped that this initiative will receive a continuance of funding after the initial year expires. An integral part of the training function of ambulance services in general, and Durham in particular, is to audit the clinical performance of staff and the treatment given to patients. Durham is one of the leading services in the country in this area and the results of audit are fed back into training programmes to ensure that all patients receive a consistent, high quality level of care.

On 27th February 1997, after considerable work in its staff training, the Trust was awarded recognition as an 'Investor in People'. This national standard reflects that an employer is committed to staff development in pursuit of its business needs and recognises the training and development strategy of the organisation and the delivery of that strategy to the staff it employs. There were many other developments taking place during these years, which have been described in the relevant sections, but it is true to say that considerable change, particularly in culture took place between 1994 and 1999. It was probably not recognised at the time how radical the changes were, as the phased nature of change during this period masked to some extent the full impact of the process.

Conclusion

The service has progressed over more than 50 years to the extent that it is safe to say that it will now be almost unrecognisable to either the staff or the patients who knew the service in the early days. This is attested to by a Mrs Foster from Wolsingham who commented as follows:
'-when I was 14 (1948) my mother was a constant attender at the Durham County Hospital and had to have ambulance transport. When this was required my father had to go to our GP to obtain a note, then go to a telephone box and book the ambulance. They were more like glorified cattle wagons with no heating and very few blankets, we even had to take a bowl with us in case of sickness, in fact, the journey was worse than attending the hospital. My father had to pay 7/6d (37.5p) for each journey, that was a lot of money in 1948. There was no hospital at Bishop Auckland then, so we all had to go to Durham or Newcastle. At the present time we ring the surgery to book the ambulance with no charge and we are guaranteed a well equipped, warm ambulance with highly trained staff who can deal with any emergency that may arise.'

Thankfully, in the whole of its history the Durham County Ambulance Service never had to face a major 'multiple casualty incident'. This is despite the fact that the County contains Teesside International Airport, the main East Coast Railway, a major motorway, and numerous busy trunk roads. The traditional industries of the north, steel, coal, heavy engineering and petro-chemicals all contribute heavy traffic on to these roads and nuclear products are carried through the county, so there are all the ingredients for potential disaster. With the exception of the industrial accident at Consett Steel Works in the 1950s, the last major incident took place on 5th January 1946 prior to the formation of the Durham service.

Following an accident to a south-bound goods train at Browney Signal Box, just south of Durham, a north-bound express train ran into debris littered across the track. As a result ten passengers were killed and eight more badly injured, but the casualty figures would have been much higher if ambulance crews had not reached the largely inaccessible site at an early stage. The way in which the ambulance crews responded is remarkable, for not only were they commended for their prompt action, it must be understood that there was no co-ordination of emergency response in those days.

Yet, despite the fact that no major incident has occurred since this time, the service has never taken matters for granted and each year exercises (like the one at Teesside Airport pictured overleaf) are undertaken to prepare ambulance crews for what might happen. That the service has progressed is without question. That it has further to go is undeniable. As this book goes to press the Secretary of State for Health, Mr Frank Dobson, has approved plans to merge the Durham and Northumbria services. On 1st April 1999, the new North East Ambulance Service NHS Trust will come into being. It will combine the best practices and traditions from the previous ambulance trusts and has been proposed to ensure that the best possible care for patients is provided to all of the communities in the North East Of England in the future.

All the ambulance services nationally are facing a substantial challenge in meeting the new performance standards that are due to be introduced in 2001. These dictate that incoming emergency calls should be prioritised into Category A (life-threatening) and Category B (serious but not life-threatening). Ambulance services will have to arrive at 75% of all Category A calls within 8 minutes and all other calls will have to be arrived at within the existing standard time of 19 minutes. In both the rural and densely populated parts of the North East, this requirement will provide its own particular challenge.

The challenges of providing regional ambulance services in the new millennium can only be assisted by the savings that will be achieved by the merger of the two existing services. In turn these savings will then be re-invested in additional staff, new ambulances and the all-important advances in training. Many other measures that will have an impact on achieving the new standard will be introduced or expanded across the North East service area. These include rapid response motorcycles and cars, the extended use of air ambulances, the training and operation of community first responders.

A major step forward will be the introduction of computerised technology, which will accurately predict the location of emergency calls and in turn allow the ambulance to be mobile before the actual call is received.

In addition to this is the certainty that communications systems will shortly undergo a radical change, and the introduction of Terrestrial Trunked Radio (TETRA) and the Public Service Radio Communication Programme (PSRCP) are examples of this change. TETRA is a digital radio standard that will allow the expansion of existing data and voice channels to users, whilst PSRCP is a project headed by the police services on a national level. As the police are currently having to renew their own radio network, they will be using TETRA for the upgrade and it is envisaged that ambulance and other emergency services will be able to access the new network if they so desire. There are really exciting times ahead for the ambulance services nationally, as well as locally, but it is equally important that we never forget our heritage. This book has aimed to chart the progress made by **The Durham County Ambulance Service** in the last 50 years. That the resulting publication commemorates the end of an era is without question, but in reality it also marks the beginning of a new chapter of public service.

The idea that this book should be produced to coincide with the dissolution of the Trust came from the chairman, Mrs Pat Wynne CBE, after her visit to the National Ambulance Exhibition (AMBEX) held at Harrogate in 1998. Following a discussion with Professor Alan Earnshaw on the British Ambulance Society's museum stand, this book was born. Alan has subsequently edited the book, volunteering his services as a leading transport historian as his contribution to the project.

However, without the memories, experiences and considerable help of the **Durham County Ambulance Service Retired Members Association** this publication would have been impossible to produce. Their assistance and encouragement is very much appreciated. In addition I must express my thanks to Karl Hannon, who did so much of the research to ensure, as far as is possible, the accuracy of the information contained in this work.

Thanks are also due to the Cleveland Ambulance Service NHS Trust and the staff of Redcar Ambulance Station for the use of their 1965 Commer ambulance, formerly a Civil Defence vehicle from the North Riding of Yorkshire which was photographed with a new Durham Transit for the cover picture.

With regard to the many photographs that appear in this book, may I say that I am indebted to the numerous contributors but special thanks are due to Joe Broadbent, Alan Croskill (Cleveland Ambulance Service), Chris Batten, Ron Henderson (Northumbria Ambulance Service), Enid Walton, the Ian Middlemass Partnership, Jim Lawson at Beamish Museum, Dennis Sherer of Vauxhall Motors and the staff of Durham County Council's archives and libraries.

On the publication side thanks are also due to the staff of Trans-Pennine Publishing, and acknowledgement should be expressed to 'Barney' Trevivian of Truro and Tim Sarginson of Kent Valley Printers who worked tirelessly to get the book produced at very short notice.

Finally, can I acknowledge the services of the many people who have checked the book for historical and factual accuracy, including members of the British Ambulance Society, Jean Hemingway, Gordon O'Brien, David Marshall and Bill McAdam. If I have failed to acknowledge any individual or organisation, can I offer my apology and thanks. The contributions, great and small, have been from so many quarters that my memory has no doubt failed me!

Thank you all.